TOO MANY PEO

Crowded street, Delhi. Photography Peter Barker/Panos Pictures

TOO MANY PEOPLE

Sir Roy Calne FRS

Introduction by Terry Waite

CALDER PUBLICATIONS • RIVERRUN PRESS
London   Montreuil   New York

First published in Great Britain in 1994 by
Calder Publications Limited
9-15 Neal Street, London WC2H 9TU

and in the United States of America in 1994 by
Riverrun Press Inc
1170 Broadway, New York, NY 10001

British Library Cataloguing-in-Publication Data
A catalogue record for this book is available from the British Library

Library of Congress Cataloging-in-Publication Data
A catalog record for this book is available from the Library of Congress

ISBN 0-7145-4269-5

Typeset in 11/13 point Times New Roman by Association Calder, Montreuil and
Spooner Graphics, London NW5.
Printed and bound in Great Britain by Ebenezer Baylis & Son Ltd, Worcester.

To my wife without whose continuing encouragement this book would not have been written, and to my children in the hope that they will be able to live and let live.

ACKNOWLEDGEMENTS

I take full responsibility for the opinions in this book. They are my own, but I gratefully acknowledge help and criticism from the following who have given valuable advice:

Professor John Aitken
Dr Derek Bromhall
Miss Celia Wai Kin Chan
Professor Y. Ebide
Dr Charles Elliott
Dr Juan M. Flavier
Mr Fulton Gillespie
Professor John Guillebaud
Mr Nick Hoffman
Dr Gordon Koch
Dr Stephen Lock
Sir John Lyons
Mrs Stefania Mazzoni
Mr Ben Milstein
Dr Paul Nicholson
Dr Max Perutz
Rev Canon Anthony Phillips
Professor Malcolm Potts
Mr Alan Rose
Dr Johnathan Steinberg
Sir Kenneth Stuart
Mr Terry Waite
Professor Keith Ward
Mrs Primrose Wayman
Dr Elizabeth Williams
Dr John Yates

It has been a privilege to have had Mr Terry Waite as a friend and colleague in Trinity Hall during the last two years. I have learned from him a lesson in courage and I thank him for his generous Foreword.

I am especially grateful to my old friend Mr Peter Somerset Fry who, with his immense experience of writing, kindly went through the text, and to Mrs Cathy Riethoff for her endless patience with the typescript.

My thanks also to Mr Phillip Ball and the Department of Medical Photography for their help in the preparation of the figures.

CONTENTS

page

AUTHOR'S PREFACE 'There is not much time left'   13

EXPLANATION : WHY I HAVE WRITTEN THIS BOOK   17

Chapter 1 Is There a Real Problem?   19
    World Population
    The Environment
    The Reality of the Problem

Chapter 2 Biological Behaviour in Animals   24

Chapter 3 Evolution and Inheritance   28
    Charles Darwin
    Gregor Mendel and Genetics
    The Molecular Basis of Inheritance

Chapter 4 Human Nature & its Consequences up to the Development
    of Gunpowder   39
    What is special about Man?
    Personality and Memory
    Early Civilisations
    Conscience and Sense of Humour
    Human Attributes
    Sin
    Altruism
    Gunpowder to Nuclear Weapons

Chapter 5 Science and Art   52
    The Scientific Method
    Copernicus
    Galileo
    Newton
    Harvey
    The Technological Exploitation of Science
    Contemporary Medicine-Application of the Scientific Method
    The Doctor's Dilemma
    Travel and Communication
    Nuclear Energy
    Molecular Biology
    Art
    The Commercialisation of Art
    The Motivation of Scientific Enquiry

Chapter 6 The Rape of the Earth and the Journey towards Self-Destruction —The Rudderless Super Tanker Heading for the Rocks   63

Chapter 7 New Killing Technology   67
Chemical
Bacterial and Viral
Nuclear Weapons
The Risks of a Nuclear Catastrophe

Chapter 8 Can Political Regimes Respond to the Dangers?   71
Failure to learn from Experience
The Power of Economic Superiority
Singapore
Rights of the Individual *v* General Good
Gun laws
Employment
Recreational Activities
Education
Ageing
Euthanasia
'Utopia'?

Chapter 9 Biology of Human Reproduction   84
Sexual Reproduction
Contraception

Chapter 10 Sex-Drive, Family Aspirations & National Ambitions   94
Cloning
An Understanding of our DNA and the Potential and Dangers of Genetic Engineering
Transgenic and Transfecting Technology
What are the Possible Consequences of Genetic Engineering?
Sexual Reproduction — Individuals are Custodians of the DNA of the Species

Chapter 11 Short-term Remedies for Urgent Action   102
An Understanding of Science
Teaching Science
Economic Environmental Conflict

Chapter 12 Long-term Goals   **107**
    The Use of National Resource
    How Valuable is One's Life?
    Unlocking Pandora's Box
    Crime and Punishment
    A Major Conceptual Change will take Time
    The Right to Reproduce
    The Aggressive Unemployed Men

Chapter 13 A Scientific Approach to Control of Population —
    A United Nations Laboratory for Population Studies   **115**
    Population Control: The Most Urgent Task for the United Nations
    Co-operative Action
    The Laboratory for Population Studies

Chapter 14 Practical Considerations   **124**

Epilogue. Man Cannot Live By Bread Alone   **127**

Hypothesis. The Creator's Testament to Modern Man   **129**

Appendix I. DNA The Template of Life   **131**

Appendix 2. Population Summit of the World's Scientific Academies   **133**

ILLUSTRATIONS

Frontis   Crowded Street, Delhi. Photograph Peter Barker/
               Panos Pictures

Figure 1   Foreword   Drawing of Terry Waite by Roy Calne   11

Figure 2   Child with Flies. Photograph by Paul Grover   22

Figure 3   Where Do We Come From? What Are We? Where Are We
               Going? by Paul Gauguin. Courtesy of Tompkins Collection,
               Museum of Fine Arts, Boston   29

Figure 4   Diagram of Dominant Mendelian Inheritance   33

Figure 5   Diagram of Recessive Mendelian Inheritance   33

Figure 6   Diagram of Structure of DNA   35

Figure 7   Diagram of DNA/RNA. Transcription for Protein Synthesis   35

Figure 8   Replication of DNA   37

Figure 9   Gaussian Curve   37

Figure 10   Fresco: Adam and Eve by Masaccio. Courtesy of
               Olivetti/Electa   44

Figure 11   Mitosis   85

Figure 12   Meiosis — Female   87

Figure 13   Meiosis — Male   87

Figure 14   Courting Dance of the Bluefoot Booby by Roy Calne   90

Figure 15   Mrs Davina T, now seven years after the transplantation
               of the heart, lungs and liver   108

Figure 16   Science: The Fruit of the Tree of Knowledge by Roy Calne.
               Courtesy of The Science Museum, London   128

FOREWORD

Roy Calne is the most unpretentious of men. He is one of those rare individuals who, whilst being quite brilliant as a transplant surgeon, refuses to be deluded by success. A visit to his Cambridge home gives a picture of the real Roy Calne, the family man, the host, the traveller, the doctor, the artist and, not least, the compassionate friend to so many. The house is decorated with artefacts from distant lands. His wife Patsy has been an essential support when there has been sadness and disappointment during the many long years of effort to make organ transplantation a life saving treatment for his patients.

Terry Waite by Roy Calne

His studio is littered with sketches and half-finished canvases. Here and there I recognise a face, a former colleague from Trinity Hall, Cambridge, a Cabinet Minister, an old lady whom I met in London who told me her life had been saved by the professor. A large brightly-coloured canvas dominates the room. Adam and Eve are portrayed, Eve receiving the fruit of the tree of knowledge, succumbing to the serpent's temptation, Adam looking worried, perhaps anticipating the troubles that will follow. Within the enormous circle of the forbidden fruit, scientific developments are symbolically represented. 'There lies a terrible warning' says Roy. 'If we continue to multiply without constraint or consideration — if we succumb to the temptations of greed, envy and hatred, the resources of this planet will be exhausted and if there are any humans remaining they will be left desolate.'

Roy has the discipline and training of a scientist. He also possesses the intuition of an artist. Above all he is a humanitarian. His many travels, particularly throughout the Far East, have convinced him that with a growth in population, which creates the equivalent of a new Los Angeles every twelve days, the situation facing our planet is grave. His scientific side recognises that science has contributed to this enormous global problem and must bear responsibility for seeking a solution. His recommendation for urgent action by the United Nations in developing a global 'think tank', a Laboratory for Population Studies, is certainly worthy of the most serious consideration.

New developments in contraception raise religious, ethical and political questions which are controversial and disturbing. The time is long overdue for a 'stepping-up' of the dialogue between scientists and those who would offer ethical formulations for the guidance of society. Sir Roy's artistic leaning constantly reminds him of the complexity of human nature, and he makes no claim in this book to provide all the answers. He admits his limited knowledge of some of the issues about which he writes, but nobody could have comprehensive expertise in such a wide-ranging analysis, which is essential even to a partial understanding of our predicament. He has deliberately not produced an academic treatise, but a lively contribution to one of the most important debates of the twentieth century. Above all, these pages reflect Roy Calne the humanitarian. He himself has made the most adequate summary in his imagined advice from the Creator to Modern Man:

> You will have many hard decisions to make but I have given you the ability to choose. In the spirit of love and compassion towards your fellow men and all living creatures, animals and plants, use your scientific knowledge to choose and act wisely to devise ways of sharing without exploitation, to live and let live.

In a world where one billion people live in acute poverty the issues raised in this book must continue to concern us all.

TERRY WAITE

AUTHOR'S PREFACE

'There is not much time left'

I pick up my pen in Cochin to record some simple observations, which seem to me to be important. Cochin is a beautiful natural port in Kerala, south west India, with a recorded history of some two thousand years, preceded by legends of even earlier civilisation. Although predominantly Hindu, Cochin has been a meeting place for Buddhists, Taoists, Muslims, Jews, Catholics and Protestants, who have traded and settled in this tolerant city. Not very far from Cochin, in north-eastern Sri Lanka, is a persecuted Tamil minority which seeks separate statehood by means of armed conflict. The 'Tamil Tigers' regard themselves as heroic freedom fighters, but the Singalese and Indians label them terrorists. No one doubts their bravery. Men and women 'Tigers' forgo alcohol, gambling and sex; they have no hesitations at killing fellow men and some are happy to sacrifice themselves to certain death for the sake of their cause, carrying explosives on their bodies into the heart of the enemy. India has already lost two heads of State, mother and son, both victims of fanatical and suicidal assassins. The population of India, which they had hoped to control, is daily increasing at an alarming rate, and it is estimated that it will exceed that of China, 1,100 million, in the next fifty years. In the large cities millions dwell in the streets on the verge of starvation in an environment of filth, disease and lack of sanitation.

The atmosphere of the big cities is polluted by millions of cars, lorries and thousands of factories, which belch out their acrid fumes while consuming irreplaceable fossil fuels. A minority are well off; politicians, business men, high ranking officers, lawyers, doctors and those rich through criminal activities. They live in elegant houses, with up to ten servants per family and enough money to buy expensive luxuries. In this grim picture, by contrast, there is also great charity and many, unselfish people devote their lives to the poor and the sick. Mother Teresa is a beacon of this compassion between humans. Family bonds are strong and supportive in both poor and rich, and the elderly are cared for and listened to.

I start with these remarks on India because it possesses, in extreme forms, easily observed attributes that categorise the human condition. Enlightened Indian politicians recognise that there can be no solution to the country's terrible poverty unless the population increase is halted, but voluntary birth control has not worked and society is out of control not only in India, but in many other countries as well.

My credentials to write on these matters are thin. I am a European with six children and no special knowledge of history, philosophy, politics or religion but I have had a biological, scientific and medical training and the nature of my work, human organ transplantation, involves constant confrontation with human despair, pain and fear. I am often asked if transplanting organs can be justified. For my patients an affirmative answer is obvious. From the point of view of society and of its national resources the question is debatable, and for mankind in general it is irrelevant. Medicine, my profession, is, after all, partly responsible for our present predicament. In most animal and plant species the number of seeds or eggs that are produced is far in excess of the individual progeny that will survive. This bountiful fecundity of nature is balanced against the adversities of the environment, where predators, pestilence, floods and drought will claim many and often most of the fertilised eggs. Humans are no exception to this biological overproduction, but in developed nations early adversities have now been almost eliminated so that death in infancy and childbirth is rare. One only needs to read a nineteenth-century novel or biography to learn how common were these calamities one hundred to two hundred years ago. They were part of life and accepted as such. Modern medicine has changed this completely. Obstructed labour can be dealt with by caesarean section, lethal infection of women after childbirth is a rarity. These benefits of scientific medicine are now being adopted by developing nations where children seldom die of measles, poliomyelitis and diphtheria, and smallpox has been eradicated. But the problem is that parents in poor countries want many children to help with the family income and to look after them in old age. Hence the tremendous rise in population in developing countries, that have developed good death control, but no birth control. As Malthus the nineteenth-century English clergyman and philosopher pointed out, the earth's resources are limited, and even with scientific developments, food production will eventually not be able to keep pace with the increasing number of mouths to feed. This was written even before medicine had reduced the chances of dying young.

Two of the most prestigious scientific academies in the world, the Royal Society and the American National Academy of Sciences recently published a warning :

> World population is growing at the unprecedented rate of almost 100 million people every year, and human activities are producing major changes in the global environment. If current predictions of population growth prove accurate and patterns of human activity on the planet remain unchanged, science and technology may not be able to prevent either irreversible degradation of the environment or continued poverty for much of the world.

Sixteen hundred scientists including a hundred and two Nobel Laureates have published a similar warning to humanity,[1] but so far, the practical response to this warning has been minimal. I find this a dreadful indictment of the relationship of society to science. We are on a disaster course, like a megatanker heading for rocks with its steering gear broken. Unless we mend this gear urgently the ship will be wrecked. There is not much time left. This is the reason why I have had the audacity to examine these matters. Let me quote another authority:

> The populations of some species spend most of their history in periods of rapid growth. Such species are called 'fugitive'. Whenever a population

[1] 'Warning to Humanity' issued in Washington by The Union of Concerned Scientists (UCS) 17 November 1992. 'Human beings and the natural world are on a collision course,' which 'may so alter the living world that it will be unable to sustain life in a manner that we know.'

reaches an unsustainable density in a given area, resources become quickly depleted and local extinction follows: part of the population starves to death, while the remainder emigrates to more hospitable sites. At the end of the twentieth century, Homo Sapiens is about to complete the list of fugitive species. The only difference is that the critical level of overpopulation will not be exceeded locally; it is the total space available that comes close to saturation. We stand on the edge of a global catastrophe and we must act soon.[2]

A conference on population growth of science academies from many nations was held in New Delhi 24-27 October 1993. The President, Sir Michael Atiyah stated in his inaugural speech :

Most of the problems we face are ultimately consequences of the progress of Science, so we must acknowledge a collective responsibility. Fortunately science also opens up possibilities of alleviating our problems, and we must see that they are pursued.

Representatives of fifty-seven National Scientific Academies signed the conference statement, reproduced in Appendix 2.

---

[2] Dr R. Ferrière, Department of Ecology and Evolutionary Biology, University of Arizona, Tucson. *The Lancet* p. 482 vol. 342, 21 August 1993

Let 1994 be remembered as the year when the people of the world decided to act together for the benefit of future generations.
Population Summit of the World's Scientific Academies
New Delhi, October 1993

EXPLANATION: WHY I HAVE WRITTEN THIS BOOK

I wish to consider the catastrophic increase in world population, the rape of the environment and the approaching disaster. I will suggest possible strategies that might help to slow down the number of human beings produced and the damage that we are causing to the rest of the world. More long-term speculations will occupy the last chapters. These include a plea to the UN to establish an international laboratory of population studies, and for individual countries to harness scientific resources towards devising a means to control human fertility appropriate to the new evolutionary force resulting from low maternal and child death rates. A change in the genetic programme to decrease fertility after bearing two children would in theory solve the problem but we are not able to do this, lacking the required knowledge and technical ability. A contraceptive vaccine could achieve the same objective administered after two normal pregnancies, but if it could be produced, how could it be distributed? The concept of an effective birth control vaccine underlines the urgent need to limit population growth in an humane manner that does not involve starvation or murder.

The growth of population, the harm it is already causing and the utter disaster that will be the eventual result, are complex subjects. As indicated in the Preface, biology, human nature, medicine, politics, greed, envy, fear and dwindling natural resource all intermingle, painting a mosaic which must be looked at as a whole to gain an understanding. Of course to do this logically, it is necessary to examine each of the coloured tiles and then try to fit them together like a jigsaw puzzle.

The stimulus to write this short book was my concern as a surgeon that my profession, medicine, together with the teaching and practice of hygiene, are largely responsible for the imbalance between births and deaths, leading to the population explosion, that can only be curtailed in an humane manner by birth control. The alternative is famine, disease, destruction of the environment and inevitably even greater human conflict.

Human nature has not changed, the primary instincts are to eat, drink and multiply. To live together in a community requires rules and a means to enforce them to prevent anarchy. The apparatus of all governments is based on an hierarchy the stability of which is normally reinforced by religion and an army. The result is sometimes recognisable as a sense of national identity with pride, patriotism and often aggressive tendencies towards neighbours as components of that identity.

The ecological balance of humans with other animals, plants and the environment was not gravely disturbed until the application of science. Medicine, jet travel, industry, new killing machines and nuclear energy have upset the balance: the uncontrolled development of these scientific applications are now threatening to destroy all life and irretrievably damage the environment.

Since the scientific method is so effective, it is the only approach that has any chance of restoring the balance between man and the rest of the world. To control the aggressive side of human nature, the gross inequality between rich and poor nations, and the wealthy and the underclass in prosperous communities, must be reduced. These dangerous divisions are increasing because our excellent death control is not balanced by birth control. The frightening population increase is visible mainly in poor nations and the underclass of rich societies. The only humane solution to this impending catastrophe is to use every means available to introduce effective birth control where it is needed. Politicians and religious leaders must realise that the facts cannot be disputed and failure to accept the challenge will lead to their personal downfall and the danger of anarchy and nuclear conflict. The application of science that has caused the instability must be harnessed to the urgent task of catching the runaway beast. Appropriate action may require the stimulus of a major disaster, which given the present international tensions, is unfortunately inevitable.

Chapter 1

Is There a Real Problem?

World Population

In its 1991 report on World Population, the United Nations Population Fund (UNFPA) states that population growth is even faster than forecast in its report of 1984. Assuming, nevertheless, that there will in the future be substantial and sustained falls in fertility rates, the global population is expected in the UN's mid-range projection to rise from 5.4 billion in 1991 to 10 billion in 2050. This rapid rise may be unavoidable; considerably larger rises must be expected if fertility rates do not stabilise at the replacement level of about 2.1 children per woman. At present, about 95% of this growth is in the less developed countries; the percentage of global population that live in the less developed countries is projected to increase from 77% in 1990 to 84% in 2020.

An optimist surveys a glass of beer and declares 'It is half full,' the same glass to a pessimist is half empty. We sometimes change from one attitude to the other depending on our mood but the fact remains that half of the glass is empty and half is full. Thomas Robert Malthus spent many years studying population and world resources and his conclusion was definitely pessimistic. Many have scorned Malthus because his predictions have not yet been fulfilled. He was an interesting man, born with a cleft palate in a middle class family. He read mathematics and theology at Cambridge achieving the position of 9th Wrangler in the university mathematics exam.[3] He was ordained into the Church of England and eventually had his own parish in Walesby, Lincolnshire. His essay on 'The principle of population' was published in 1798. Malthus was the first to study and analyse a universal and perpetual dilemma: he maintained that the prospects for a permanent improvement in the condition of the masses in society in all countries was placed in a precarious balance by an unequal race between the hare of population growth and a tortoise which represented the ability of agriculture to expand food production. He used mathematical arguments to show that population increased in a geometric fashion by a given ratio, whilst increase in food production could only be by a given (much smaller) amount. Thus population might double every fifty years whilst production of food would increase by 1,000 tons each year, an arithmetical progression. The 'Malthusian' concept has become part of our vocabulary, used in scientific and popular debate on the problems of population growth especially in developing nations, and by environmentalists who regard the balance between population and exhaustible resources as a global problem.

Astronomers disagree amongst themselves on fundamental concepts of the

---

[3] The hierarchy of Cambridge Mathematics was graded as first to tenth Wrangler, depending on how many passed the final examination.

cosmos but most agree that eventually conditions on earth will not be able to support life. After millions of years the expansion of the sun will grill the solar system, which will then cool to extremely low temperatures. The time scale is so vast as to be meaningless to most people as a reason for changing our behaviour. Our descendants, if we have any, may plan to colonise another planet as the earth's temperature becomes intolerable. But what if the earth were to be unable to sustain life, or at least the life of man and other mammals in a hundred years' time or even less? Surely such a prediction should concentrate the mind exceedingly. If we continue our so-called 'progress' in the direction in which we are headed at present, many experts would maintain that one hundred years is an overgenerous estimate.

The Environment

Although there is a relationship between population, economic activity, and the environment, it is not simple. Most of the environmental changes during the twentieth century have been a product of the efforts of humans to secure improved standards of food, clothing, shelter, comfort and recreation. Both developed and developing countries have contributed to environmental degradation. Developed countries, with 85% of the world's gross national product and 23% of its population, account for the majority of mineral and fossil-fuel consumption, causing an increase in atmospheric carbon dioxide, which may alter global climate and affect all countries. The prosperity and technology of the developed countries endow them with the potential and the responsibility to address environmental problems in a practical manner. Unfortunately because of the short-term thinking of industrialists looking for profit, accountants not trained to look at consequences and politicians who seldom look further ahead than the next election, this *responsibility* tends to be neglected.

In the developing countries the resource consumption per capita is lower, but the rapidly growing population and the pressure to develop their economies are leading to substantial and increasing damage to the local environment. This damage comes by direct pollution from energy use and other industrial activities, as well as by such activities as the clearing of forests and inappropriate agricultural and irrigation practices which deplete irreplaceable water supplies.

The Reality of the Problem

Scientific and technological innovations in agriculture have been able to overcome many past pessimistic predictions about resource constraints affecting human welfare. Nevertheless, the present patterns of human activity, accentuated by population growth, should make even those who are most optimistic about future scientific progress pause to reconsider the wisdom of ignoring the threats to our planet. The unrestrained resource consumption of energy and food production, as the developing world strives to achieve living standards similar to the developed world, will lead to a catastrophic deterioration of the global environment.

Some of the environmental changes may produce irreversible damage to the earth's capacity to sustain life. Many species of plant and animal have already disappeared, and many more are destined to do so. The wild tiger is nearly extinct. Man's own prospects for achieving satisfactory living standards are threatened by environmental deterioration, especially in the poorest countries where economic activities are most heavily dependent upon natural resources.

To quote from the Royal Society and National Academy of Sciences warning:

> If they are forced to deal with their environmental and resource problems alone, the less developed countries face overwhelming challenges. They generate only 15% of the world's gross national product, and have a net cash outflow of tens of billions of dollars per year. Over 1 billion people live in absolute poverty, and 600 million on the margin of starvation. And the less developed countries have only 6-7% of the world's active scientists and engineers, a situation that makes it very difficult for them to participate fully in global or regional schemes to manage their own environment. In places where resources are administered effectively, population growth does not inevitably imply deterioration in the quality of the environment. Nevertheless, each additional human being requires natural resources for sustenance, each produces by-products that become part of the ecosystem, and each pursues economic and other activities that affect the natural world. While the impact of population growth varies from place to place and from one environmental domain to another, the overall pace of environmental changes has unquestionably been accelerated by the recent expansion of the human population.

There are many different assessments of population statistics, and their accuracy must vary, but all agree that human numbers are growing world-wide, very little perhaps in north west Europe and the USA, but at a staggering rate in most developing countries. If each married couple had two children, the population would remain static, provided most young people married. The average number of two is however increased by from 50% to three or more in most developing countries. Meanwhile the average life span almost everywhere is increasing, although famine, drought and AIDS have taken their toll of life in Africa. In western Europe and the USA males live an average of seventy years and females seventy-five years. In India the figures are sixty and sixty-five. The enormous increase in the numbers of living humans, combined with their prolonged life span, which is mainly a result of modern medicine, confront the availability of world resources, whether animal, vegetable or mineral. Already the increase in mechanised farming, in fishing and the use of insecticides has changed the environment, even without taking into account the commercial greed and exploitation that is destroying forests, removing fossil fuels and releasing nuclear waste. The production of food for humans is raping the earth, taking away its natural riches and giving nothing

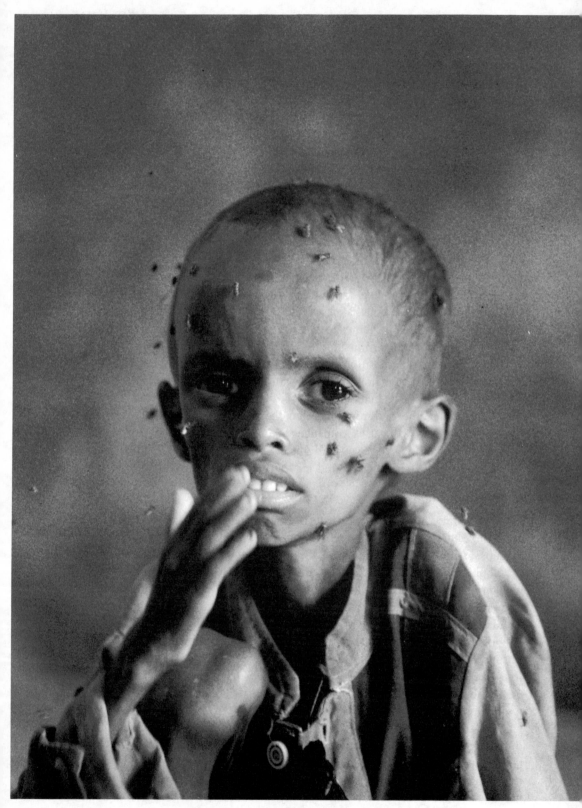

Figure 2. Child with Flies. Photograph by Paul Grover

back. The over-production of Western farming can never feed the starving poor because there are far too many hungry mouths already. Shortage of fresh water is likely to be the most serious deficiency in the next decade.[4]

If a pestilence such as AIDS does not kill humans on the scale that is predicted, the quality of life for the poor will get worse, not only in Africa, but in all underdeveloped areas. The sadness and human misery caused by widespread starvation in Africa have been seen in our homes on the television screen. We are confronted with emaciated, despairing, dying human beings. Numerous pathetic mothers, infants and children usually predominate in the scenes of this obscene tragedy, often made especially poignant by reports of armed, politically motivated soldiers preventing relief food from reaching the children. So they die in a manner which is a disgrace to humanity. How much better if birth control had prevented their conception rather than for them to be killed by starvation after two or three years of miserable life! (*figure* 2).

It is hard to refute these observations, but in each case there will be those who cover their shame and embarrassment by saying that the circumstances were 'exceptional'. Rational people must accept the facts. Death through starvation is a real problem, which is accelerating at an alarming rate. It should be the main item of concern of all human beings, but especially of national governments and of the United Nations.

In order to discuss this subject and to comprehend it properly, it is necessary to examine the biology of men and of animals, of reproduction, human nature, politics, religion and the relationship of these to the application of science.

[4] Peter H. Gleick: *Water in Crisis: A guide to the World's Fresh Water Resources*, Oxford Science Publications 1993

Chapter 2

Biological Behaviour in Animals

The remarkable patience and perseverance of field biologists, armed with modern video technology, has provided us with a scientific record of importance and some of the most beautiful and informative television which it has been our good fortune to receive in the comfort of our homes, without having to climb up giant trees or descend into dangerous caverns. The adaptation of animals and plants to their environment and to change, and their coexistence, involves the most extraordinary variations in body structure, nutrition, reproduction and social behaviour.

The welding together of communities of ants and termites 'one for all and all for one' is a life-style that is apparently dedicated to the survival of their colonies. Individual lives are of no importance in the common objective to protect and feed the queen who lays the eggs; the only role of the male is to fertilise the queen. The termite workers spend their lives constructing beautiful living quarters with complicated access and ventilation shafts designed to protect the inmates from the rigours of the environment and from predators. Ants of similar appearance, but from a different colony, who trespass on the territory of another nest, are rapidly eliminated in what we would regard as a vicious and efficient killing manoeuvre. Despite these elaborate precautions, as any bee-keeper knows, colonial insects may develop parasitic diseases and the larger parasites have smaller parasites. There are also subtle dangers. Predatory wasps have learned to evade the bees on sentry duty by acquiring the special odour of the colony and by creeping into the hive with a 'false passport', they can steal food that has been carefully stored by the worker bees and kill any bees they encounter. The naked mole rat and meerkats are mammalian colonial animals living in well-structured societies. In the naked mole rat community a female is selected as the breeding queen of the colony.

Much nearer to man in biological terms, chimpanzees lead a life that probably has similarities to our ancestors. They have loose but complicated social arrangements and usually the most physically powerful and agile male will fight off other male rivals to mate with females as they come on heat, but there is also evidence of mate selection not solely resting on brute force. After mating the males then go off hunting, often having little contact with the females they have impregnated, nor the babies when they are born, but they will return to the females when once again they are sexually receptive. Females nurture the babies and look after them until they can fend for themselves. Chimpanzees will eat animal and vegetable matter and can hunt together in an extremely purposeful manner in the trees to catch and devour other creatures, including monkeys, which they will often consume along with vegetables, a mixed 'meat and veg' diet.

A rare sub-species of chimpanzee, the pigmy chimp, apparently enjoys sexual intercourse and sexual encounters with either sex, at all times, but sexual behaviour that is not directly related to reproduction is unusual in animals. The pigmy chimpanzee is not carnivorous. They are gentle creatures who do not fight, and seem rather to have a social life devoted to sexual pleasure.

The male dominated society with fighting ability that is related to success in reproduction is common in many animal species. An interesting variant of this pattern is the successful impregnation of the 'desirable' female by a weak and small male who waits until the competitive preoccupation of the powerful 'macho' combatants is maximal, and then moves rapidly in to mate the female. These 'sneaky' males were shown in the television programme *The Sexual Imperative*[5] in waterfowl and gladiatorial Hercules beetles. What happens to the vigour of the genes when the progeny, instead of resulting from mating by the powerful victor, is instead a product of the weak 'sneaky' male? I wonder if his behaviour will have a selective advantage in favour of 'intelligence', avoiding vicious combat but, nevertheless, getting the prize! The programme did not comment on the evolutionary significance.

In lions the male dominance may even appear to be counter-productive in terms of survival of the species. A violent struggle between a young vigorous lion and an old male who is head of the pride may result in the old male being usurped by the younger male. The victor will then slaughter any cubs of the old male that are in the pride, eliminating potential competitors with the old male's genes. Lions when hunting demonstrate what we would call male chauvinism. Usually the females have not only the role of bearing and rearing their cubs and incidentally sometimes seeing them murdered before their eyes by their new mate, but in hunting the females do most of the work. They hunt together but when they succeed in killing their prey it is the male who moves forward and eats his fill of the best parts of the carcass, the 'lion's share'. Only then can the females enjoy their food.

The adaptation of more primitive animals than mammals varies across an enormous spectrum. With some insects the male's role is even less attractive than the fertilising functions of a drone bee, the aggressive preying mantis tries to eat the male after he has fulfilled his reproductive role and this nutritional perquisite is very important for the female, less so one might imagine for the male. The female may even start her meal, decapitating the male, before he has finished copulating. The headless body continues mating driven by nerve impulses providentially situated below the head. In the largest species of moth called the 'Atlas' the male's role in life is strikingly apparent. It has no mouth parts and cannot eat, it has reached the stage of sexual maturation from the nutrition available as an embryo caterpillar. Its only purpose is to fertilise the female, perhaps a joyous but short-lived experience, ending in starvation.

The behaviour of lower animals may appear to us to be extremely bizarre. Many species are dependent on other species for their existence, perhaps as symbionts living in a coexisting manner with the host, or alternatively in producing a disease, for example the malarial parasite. If, however, the parasitic organism destroys the host species, then it will also become extinct. Plants are adapted according to the environment: some species can display purposeful action by catching winged and

---

[5] *The Sexual Imperative*, Genesis Films, Channel 4 Television, January 1993

crawling insects within specialised leaves and then producing digestive juices similar to those that digest food in our stomachs. Fungi are a highly diverse and specialised form of plant that do not require sunlight for their own metabolism. Bacteria are similar to fungi, and the most simple living matter of all, viruses, are still highly complicated in their *modus vivendi*. Some viruses, consisting mostly of the building bricks of life, namely nucleic acids, nevertheless have extremely specialised behaviour. After entering the cell of the host, viruses can convert the nucleic acids of the host nucleus into their own structure. Thus the AIDS virus hijacks the nucleic acid of a human white blood cell, the lymphocyte, to produce more AIDS virus. Animals infected with micro-organisms have elaborate protective devices. In man they come under the category of 'immune' mechanisms. These reside especially in lymphocytes and the destruction of the immune lymphocytes by the AIDS virus leaves the patient devoid of defence against any potential infective organism which normally would be eliminated quickly from the body. The immunologically paralysed sufferer from AIDS is therefore vulnerable to a wide variety of organisms which can contribute to his death. Generally speaking however, infective organisms will not eliminate a species, because, as mentioned above, this would not be to the advantage of the organisms. Some members of the host species will have a natural resistance to the infection and it will be these 'lucky' survivors who will be able to maintain the species and the inheritance of the resistance will ensure a robust progeny. A well known example of this was the myxoma virus, which had been expected to eliminate the rabbit population. Myxomatosis spread throughout the world and killed most of the rabbits, but there were sufficient resistant animals to survive and flourish, thereby overcoming the attempt at 'genetic cleansing' that had been intended by those who had infected wild rabbits with the myxoma virus.

I have chosen a few examples of animal behaviour to show how diverse it can be and also to demonstrate that the theme running through most biological observations is the tendency for a species to survive and reproduce. In many species the division into two sexes results in a mixing of the genetic material of nucleic acid, which gives a chance for diversity to occur in the progeny with characters that may be advantageous or the reverse. The male dominance in most species is not universal and even in mammals the opposite role model can be found. Especially interesting is the spotted hyena, in which both males and females develop long penises as cubs. Aristotle thought that the hyena was an hermaphrodite and this was the prevailing view until recently; it is, however, wrong. It has been shown that the female's penis/clitoris is used for play in cubs and as an organ of social recognition and greeting in adults. When there is a meeting of hyenas of either sex they approach each other cautiously. If the two individuals are of the same clan they first engage in muzzle licking then they expose their erect penis or clitoris to each other's tongue, a signal of great trust when one considers the traumatic potential of the hyena's bite. This elaborate ritual seems to be equivalent to our hand-shaking and is not connected to the reproductive act. Female hyenas exhibit extremely dominant and aggressive behaviour. The females are larger and stronger in combat than the males. The most powerful female will lead a pack of hyenas even to fight lions. The male is a relatively unimportant member of the clan apart from providing sperm for reproduction. This strange anatomy and the behaviour of the spotted hyena is due to the high levels of male hormones that circulate in the bloodstream of females.[6]

When man is excluded there is a wonderful balance between the hundreds of thousands of species of animals and plants. The constraints of climate, food availability, predators and disease permit the survival of successful species; organisms that are unable to compete or participate in this balance become endangered species, and after being reduced to a critical, small number that are incapable of maintaining the species by reproduction, they will become extinct. The atmosphere, land mass, seas, lakes, rivers and forests are not in danger of destruction by living organisms divorced from man. But man is also a living organism, with life processes similar to all living creatures. There are, however, important differences in man from other organisms; these will be considered later.

It is inappropriate to look at living organisms through a romantic mist. The environment can be hostile, and the changes of the Ice Ages probably destroyed many species permanently, while the behaviour of animals to one to another often offends the sensibilities of so-called 'civilised' man. Catastrophes from outside apart from the cooling of the atmosphere may destroy life, or some of the life, on earth. It is believed that large meteorites or small comets have hit our planet in the past, causing extensive damage to the earth's surface which is comparable to the destructive force of many nuclear bombs, and which eliminated numerous species of animals and plants. It is conceivable that in the future we will be able to anticipate such a catastrophe and even divert the course of collision, so that a comet heading for the earth's destruction might be shifted from its path by an atomic missile. These speculations assume that mankind and other species will still be surviving in a civilised manner at such a future time, but are we justified in this assumption? In the next chapters I will outline some of the facts and concepts relating to evolution and the inheritance of which we are a part, and describe certain features that distinguish man from other living organisms.

[6] *Science*, 25 June 1993, vol. 260, no 5116, pp 1929-31

Chapter 3

Evolution and Inheritance

In his painting (*figure* 3) 'Where do we come from? What are we? Where are we going?' Gauguin painted the conundrum of life and the universal curiosity of man to comprehend and appreciate his place in life, in a beautiful and powerful picture. He then tried to kill himself with arsenic. No doubt he wished to find out where he was going immediately, but he vomited and survived. Since written records have been available, these same questions have been an essential feature of mankind's quest for self-knowledge. Scientific answers to 'Where have we come from?' and 'Where are we going?' are only available in terms in chemistry and physics, which are clearly unsatisfactory to the enquiring mind, and the expectations of metaphysical answers seem to be inherent in human thought. Even in the most primitive tribes 'answers' are given to these questions in terms of past mythology related to the present and the future. These questions have always been of extreme importance to civilised man and the answers involve not only detailed beliefs but also a *modus vivendi* that is related to these beliefs, with rules for living that vary from moderate behaviour that is easily attained, to extremely severe and constrained lives with dire punishments for transgression. I will consider this subject in the next chapter, but here I wish to look briefly at the scientific evidence of our origins.

In his book *The Rise and Fall of the Third Chimpanzee*, Jared Diamond outlines the closeness of man to chimpanzees and of chimpanzees to other primate species, in terms of the similarity of the assembly of the structure of the DNA of the cell nucleus. There is only a 1.6% difference in the DNA of man and chimpanzees and yet we consider ourselves to be creatures of a different order. What is the justification for this? Well, in terms of biological nomenclature, we are a species distinct from the chimpanzee because fertile progeny cannot result from the mating of humans and chimpanzees. But Diamond also points out other important differences which I will discuss later. Here I would simply emphasise the obvious, that there is an extreme similarity in the arrangement of the genes of the chimpanzee and man, and one can trace the similarity of DNA throughout the primate species. This process of similarity also applies through other mammalian species, and eventually back to non-mammalian vertebrates, invertebrates, plants, fungi, bacteria and viruses. A chain of complexity is apparent with a simple virus at the one extreme and man at the other. When Darwin assembled the case for his evolutionary theory, genes and nucleic acids were unknown. Gregor Mendel had described a mathematical relationship between the appearances of plants and the predictable numerical results of crossing pure bred strains of plants of the same species with different appearances, but these observations of central importance in an understanding of inheritance were also not available to Darwin. He based his theories on prolonged and careful observation and deduction.

Like Malthus, Charles Darwin was trained in mathematics and theology at Cambridge and he came from a family distinguished in science, his grandfather

Figure 3. Where Do We Come From? What Are We? Where Are We Going? (D'ou venons-nous? Que sommes-nous? Où allons nous?) by Paul Gaugin. Tompkins Collection, courtesy of The Museum of Fine Arts, Boston.

Erasmus Darwin being particularly famous in his biological studies and theories of evolution. Darwin's father, a doctor, wanted his son to follow in his footsteps, but after a short period as a medical student in Edinburgh, Charles decided that he did not wish to become a doctor because he was so appalled by the dreadful suffering of patients subjected to surgery without anaesthesia. His school attainments were certainly insufficient to be acceptable to any Oxbridge college now, but coming from a wealthy middle-class background, he was accepted as a student of theology and mathematics at Christ's College, Cambridge. His scholastic achievements as an undergraduate were not distinguished, but he was a first class horseman and a good shot with a sporting gun. He was passionately interested in extra-curricular natural history, and he sat at the feet of the Professor of Biology and Geology, John Stevens Henslow. They became friends and Darwin's enthusiasm for, and knowledge of, biology and geology became all important to him and was to remain so for the rest of his long life. When the Admiralty was planning to chart the seas off South America, its officials approached Henslow to see if he would join the voyage as a professional biologist; when Mrs Henslow objected, her husband wondered whether the young amateur naturalist Charles Darwin might be able to take on this job. Despite considerable parental opposition the young man succeeded in obtaining the unpaid post of ship's naturalist. Darwin's eventual father-in-law who was also his uncle, Josiah Wedgewood, championed his cause and for the next five years Darwin voyaged with *The Beagle*. He suffered from terrible sea-sickness, but when *The Beagle* finally reached South America he was able to resume his interest in natural history. He travelled first down the east coast and then up the west, collecting specimens of animals, plants and fossils and putting his ideas together. He was beginning to conceive a theory as to how this extraordinary inter-relationship of the species had come about. He sought answers to the commonest question that every biology student asks when similarities of the basic structures and functions of different species of vertebrate animals are studied. It is thought that by the time *The Beagle* had reached the beautiful Galapagos Islands, Darwin's views had crystallised on a system of evolution that involved continuous variation within a species, favouring those most adapted to survive in adverse environmental conditions. The Galapagos Islands are relatively new volcanic eruptions in the Pacific close to Equador and species had evolved in the separate islands in different ways. Darwin was particularly fascinated by the adaptive evolution of animals and plants which had developed individual characteristics on each of these islands. On his return journey, Darwin had endless discussions about his theories with Captain Robert Fitzroy of *The Beagle*, who was to be a strong opponent of Darwinism later. When he returned to England, Darwin's health was impaired, but he carefully proceeded to assemble an enormous amount of data in order to make his case irresistibly strong before presenting it to the scientific community. He knew that his theories ran counter to traditional orthodox religious dogma and that they would incur public outcry against him.

The integrity of Darwin as a man can be judged by what must have been a serious shock to him when he received a long letter from another biologist, Alfred Russell

Wallace, who was writing from the remote East Indies island of Ternate where he thought he was dying from a fever. Wallace wished to explain to Darwin his own theory of evolution. Wallace had come to a similar conclusion as Darwin but with much less data. Darwin very generously acknowledged Wallace's work and the two most important papers ever given in the field of biology were read to a small audience in London on 1st July 1858 at the Linnaean Society by the Society's secretary as Darwin was grieving over the death of his son and Wallace was still in the Malay Archipelago. It was sometime before the outstanding importance of Darwin's and Wallace's theories on evolution and natural selection, with their supporting evidence, were appreciated. As Darwin had anticipated, the vituperation and personal vilification that followed were vicious. Some prominent churchmen were especially antagonistic and the famous encounter at the British Association for the Advancement of Science in Oxford, between Thomas Henry Huxley, who was Darwin's friend and champion, and Bishop Samuel Wilberforce of Oxford is related as follows:[7]

The proceedings opened quietly, not to say dully. For an hour or more Professor Draper from America rambled on about the 'intellectual development of Europe considered with reference to the views of Mr Darwin and others,' and he was followed by three other speakers who were hardly more inspired. The last of them, a man with an odd accent, began making diagrams on the blackboard. 'Let this point A be the man,' he declared, and 'let that point B be the mawnkey.' This was too much for the bored undergraduates. They had come to be entertained and entertainment they were going to have, even if they had to generate it themselves. 'Mawnkey, Mawnkey,' they roared, and refused to allow the unfortunate speaker to continue.

By now Wilberforce had entered the hall with his attendant clergy about him, and he created something of a stir with his priestly clothes and his air of confident Episcopal authority. Henslow called on him to speak, and he plunged at once with a fine flow of words into a ridicule of Darwin's 'Casual theory.' Where were the proofs? Darwin was merely expressing sensational opinions, and they went flatly against the divine revelation of the Bible. This was no more than had been expected, but the Bishop on rising to the height of his peroration went too far. He turned to Huxley, who was sitting on the platform — an arresting figure in his top-coat, his high wing-collar and his leonine black hair — and demanded to know if it was through his grandmother or his grandfather that he claimed to be descended from the apes.

It was not really the moment for heavy sarcasm, and Huxley was not a man to provoke lightly. It was by chance that he was at the meeting at all; he had met a friend in the street that morning who had persuaded him

[7] References to *Darwin and The Beagle* by Alan Moorehead

to go. Now when he heard how ignorantly the Bishop presented his case, ending with his 'insolent question', he said in undertone, 'The Lord hath delivered him into my hands.' He got up and announced that he would certainly prefer to be descended from an ape rather than from a cultivated man who prostituted the gifts of culture and eloquence to the service of prejudice and falsehood. The Bishop in short did not know what he was talking about.

One did not lightly insult the clergy in the 1860s. Uproar ensued. The undergraduates clapped and shouted, the clergy angrily demanded an apology, and the ladies from their seats under the windows fluttered their handkerchiefs in consternation. One of them, a Lady Brewster, collapsed from shock and had to be carried out.

Since that time the theory of natural selection has never been seriously challenged by scientists, although some of the data relating to it have been shown to be inaccurate. A similar selective process appears to occur in other biological systems notably in the selection of lymphocytes that are able to respond to foreign antigen, e.g. a transplanted organ graft.

GREGOR MENDEL *and Genetics*

Gregor Mendel was a Catholic monk working in Brno, at that time part of Austria. He was a keen amateur biologist, especially interested in heredity in plants. He is also an outstanding example of how totally irrelevant can be the number of publications bolstering up the 'ego' and *curriculum vitae* of a scientist. I had always thought that Mendel had written two papers but in fact I am wrong. He wrote only one, but he did present a few scientific communications to local natural history societies which preceded the one paper.[8] At these unpretentious meetings he described how he had been breeding peas and beans for some years and had been successful in obtaining varieties with different morphological characteristics e.g. tall or short variants which bred true. The purpose of growing these inbred lines was to study what happened when the lines were crossed. In the course of the next seven years, Mendel and his gardener patiently planted seeds that had been fertilised by different combinations of pure bred peas or beans. What followed was a short analysis in mathematical terms of the findings, for example how many of the progeny were tall, short or in between. When different characters were studied, Mendel was able to show that some characters would be manifest in the progeny when present in only one of the parents and were therefore called dominant (*figure* 4).Others did not appear in either parent but would nevertheless reside in a recessive form so that when parents each containing the recessive characteristic reproduced, some of the progeny would show the character as a result of the combination of the two recessive inherited features or 'genes' as they are

[8] Gregor Mendel: 'Versuche uber Planzenhybriden'Verh.naturforsch. Verein in Brunn vol. IV, 1866.

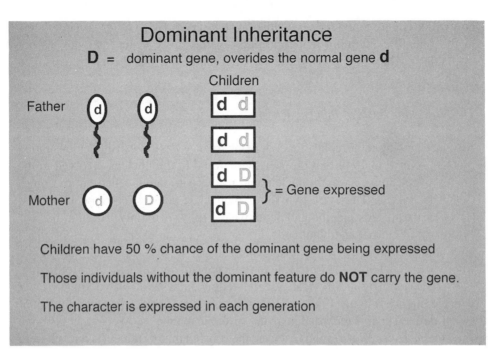

Figure 4. Diagram of Dominant Mendelian Inheritance

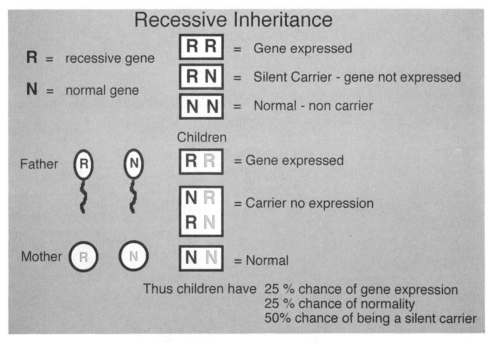

Figure 5. Diagram of Recessive Mendelian Inheritance

now called (figure 5 and *see* Appendix I). This paper of Mendel's was largely lost in the scientific literature and was rediscovered thirty years later. It was not available to Darwin but it would have strengthened his theory by giving a mechanistic basis for inheritance.

The Molecular Basis of Inheritance

An understanding of the replicating code of inheritance was to await the demonstration by O.T. Avery[9] in 1944 that the genetic material in the nucleus involved in the process of cell division was the nucleic acid arranged in strands called chromosomes (see Appendix I). There are two forms of nucleic acid, deoxyribonucleic acid (DNA) in the nucleus and ribonucleic acid (RNA) present mainly in the non-nuclear cytoplasm of animal and plant cells. For some years an exciting race took place internationally between molecular biologists as to the structural mechanism whereby the nucleic acids were able to replicate and convey genetic information. The race was won by an American research fellow, James Watson working together with the English scientist Francis Crick in Cambridge. The details of this pursuit of a well-defined goal is recorded in a very readable manner by Watson, in his book *The Double Helix*. Watson and Crick led the way but many eminent scientists were and still are important contributors to nucleic acid research.

DNA is composed of units of four bases, adenine, thymine, guanine and cytosine. These are always arranged so that adenine pairs with thymine and guanine with cytosine. There are interlocking molecules that assemble these bases into two helices for each chromosome rather like two spiral staircases running together (*figure* 6). They form the templates for the production of proteins via an intermediate messenger RNA which instructs the cell to produce specific proteins (*figure* 7); these are the working molecules of all living organisms, responsible for the intricate and complicated structure of living creatures and the metabolism of the individual parts. A single cell may produce thousands of distinct proteins. The double structure of the nucleic acid helix splits into two single parts which reproduce themselves when the cell divides (*figure* 8). The normal or 'diploid' number of chromosomes is 46 for man. Each sperm and unfertilised egg possesses half or the 'haploid' number of chromosomes of the fully fertilised egg or zygote. When the sperm and egg fuse the two haploid sets of chromosomes now make up the normal number present in every cell except the sperm and unfertilised eggs or oocytes (see Appendix I).

Within the fertilised egg is the coding for the whole living organism including its reproductive cells. By analogy, one could look upon the fertilised egg as the digital impressions in a vinyl disc, which when transcribed on an appropriate machine will produce a whole symphony. Information is encoded in condensations living being depends on the arrangement and structure of the genes, collectively called the 'genome'. The chromosomes of a zygote are programmed for first cell of DNA called genes which have individual functions. The unique nature of every

[9] O.T. Avery, Canadian bacterialist, worked at the Rockerfeller Institute, New York

Structure of DNA

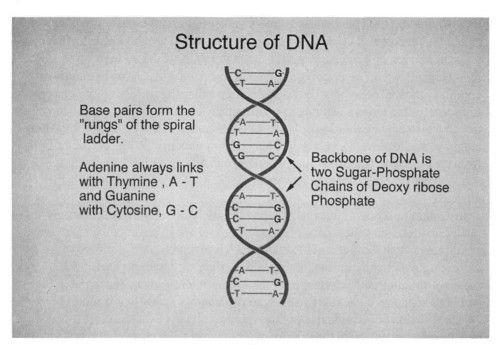

Base pairs form the "rungs" of the spiral ladder.

Adenine always links with Thymine , A - T and Guanine with Cytosine, G - C

Backbone of DNA is two Sugar-Phosphate Chains of Deoxy ribose Phosphate

Figure 6. Diagram of Structure of DNA

Transcription of RNA for Protein Synthesis

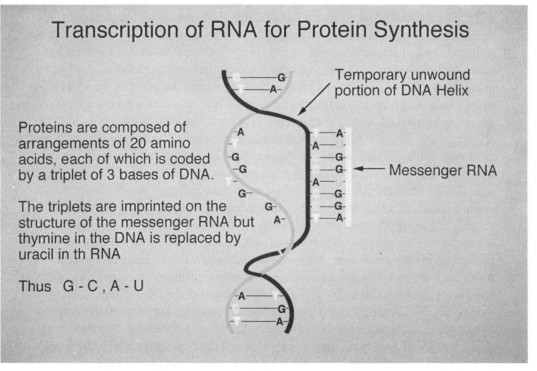

Temporary unwound portion of DNA Helix

Proteins are composed of arrangements of 20 amino acids, each of which is coded by a triplet of 3 bases of DNA.

Messenger RNA

The triplets are imprinted on the structure of the messenger RNA but thymine in the DNA is replaced by uracil in th RNA

Thus G - C , A - U

Figure 7. Diagram of DNA/RNA. Transcription for Protein Synthesis

living being depends on the arrangement and structure of the genes, collectively called the 'genome'. The chromosomes of a zygote are programmed for first cell division and all subsequent stages in the maturation of the embryo up to a free living organism with functioning organs and inscribed with certain extraordinarily complex potential behaviour patterns which we call instincts. The ability of a crow to forage for the twigs and straw to construct a nest, in a safe place at the top of a tree in which eggs will be laid and the next generation nurtured, is not something taught by an old crow to a young one, but is programmed in the egg cell of the crow from the time of fertilisation. Such wonders of nature occur in every living species and in every case the encoding resides in the genes of the chromosomes in the cell nucleus.

In explaining modern concepts of evolution, Richard Dawkins describes how the nucleic acids of the genes transcribe proteins to form a living organism and how it would appear that the secret of life in the DNA is to reproduce and evolve with ever increasing complexity an inexorable and 'selfish' programme to do 'better' by means of variation and the selection of the strongest for survival. The terms 'selfish' and 'better' in this context are used in an explanatory rather than a moral sense.

The variation of individuals provides a population in which the most successful genetic material will be in those individuals that have, 'by chance', the best ability to resist the vicissitudes of an unfriendly environment. Any given characteristic in a species will vary in degree. Sexual reproduction involves the intermingling of two different individuals' genetic material, and this applies for each characteristic, for example, the height of a plant or the strength of an arm muscle or the speed of a reflex. If these characteristics are recorded for 1000 individuals there will be a so-called bell-shaped or Gaussian frequency distribution curve in which the majority of readings will be towards the middle; a few are exceptionally short, weak or slow in the examples given, and at the other extreme a few individuals are exceptionally tall, strong or fast (*figure* 9).[10] In terms of survival, the local environment will be all-important: usually a strong individual with fast reflexes would be at an advantage but a tall individual may be at a disadvantage in scrub grass where his head will show above the top of the grass to predators who would be able to hunt him down. A short, strong individual with fast reflexes might under those circumstances do better than a tall one. A tall individual, however, would have a distinct advantage if available food is high in the trees. The giraffe is an obvious winner here. Characters with survival advantage will be selected preferentially for the species in each generation. In most mammals where the dominant male rules the roost, the females will be mated by males that are the strongest, the quickest and the fiercest (or cleverest in the case of the 'sneaky' males), and these characteristics will then be inherited by the offspring, both male and female; but the internal environment of a female is different from that of a male, due to the different sex hormones : the manifestation of fierceness may be subdued and the development of muscle may be less marked in females of the same species, with the special exception of the spotted hyena (see chapter 2).

[10] 'Gaussian' after the German mathematician Carl Friedrich Gauss 1777-1855, Professor at Göttingen University

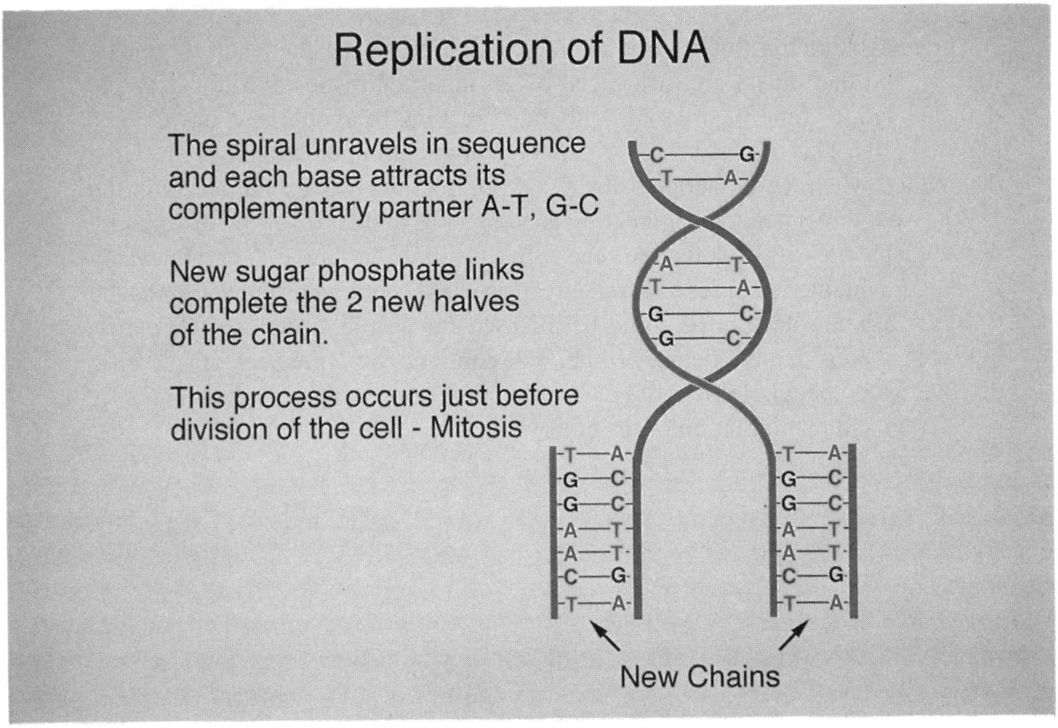

Replication of DNA

The spiral unravels in sequence and each base attracts its complementary partner A-T, G-C

New sugar phosphate links complete the 2 new halves of the chain.

This process occurs just before division of the cell - Mitosis

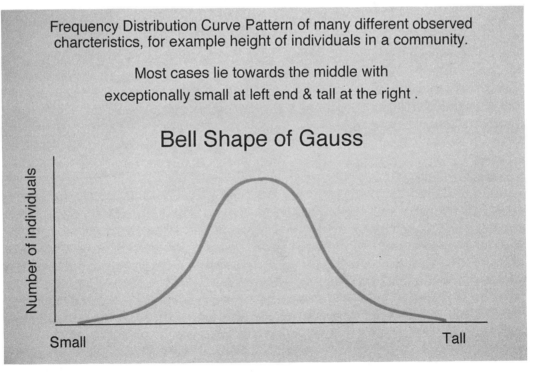

New Chains

Figure 8. Replication of DNA

Frequency Distribution Curve Pattern of many different observed charcteristics, for example height of individuals in a community.

Most cases lie towards the middle with exceptionally small at left end & tall at the right .

Bell Shape of Gauss

Number of individuals

Small

Tall

Figure 9. Gaussian Curve

The realisation that some diseases like cystic fibrosis are the result of genetic defects, and that others are influenced by an inherited disposition, for example diabetes, led to some theories of deliberate breeding to avoid these unwelcome parental gifts. This idea of selective genetic manipulation, or 'Eugenics', became discredited when it was adopted for racist political reasons by the Nazis in the 1930s. Now direct genetic engineering is being used to treat inherited diseases by replacing the missing or defective gene with a healthy alternative. A careful watch is being maintained in order to avoid any unethical genetic interference, since the techniques being developed could be misused for political purposes. There is, however, a considerable debate, which will continue, over the uses of scientific discoveries in the whole field of genetics in connection with sex selection, DNA replication and manipulation of the embryo.

Chapter 4

Human Nature and its Consequences
Up to the Development of Gunpowder

In the previous chapter I explained how the predetermined pattern responsible for animal structure function and behaviour depended on the DNA of the zygote ,and evolutionary changes occur because of the variation of the DNA resulting from sexual reproduction. Further variation occurs during reproductive cell division of the sperm and egg by exchange or 'crossing over' of portions of paired chromosomes (see Appendix I). Another mechanism of such variation follows spontaneous or induced changes in the DNA configuration called mutations, for example x-rays in large doses can destroy DNA but in smaller doses they can produce subtle chemical disturbances which may have profound effects in the development, structure, function and behaviour when DNA is passed on to offspring. The changes can be beneficial, detrimental or apparently irrelevant to evolutionary survival advantage. Certain recessive harmful genes will be manifested as diseases when complemented by a second similar recessive gene in the fertilised egg (see Appendix I). This is much more likely to occur in mating between close relations, hence the taboo against consanguineous marriage in most societies. Whatever one might wish, individual members of a species are not born equal: variation is a fact of nature.

What is Special about Man?

So far all the above considerations in animals apply also to man. Is man then merely another animal with a more complicated brain than other creatures or do humans have a qualitative difference from all other animals? In *The Rise and Fall of the Third Chimpanzee* Diamond argues strongly that the salient special characteristic of '*homo sapiens*' is language. There are many well-documented methods of communication between animals, especially developed in mate finding, access to food, territorial claims and warnings of danger. The early morning bird song is a beautiful example of the first and the dance of the honey bee announcing a source of nectar and exactly where it can be found, the second. Loud cries will in many species announce the recognition of a predator nearby. These exchanges are, however, different from language, but no doubt in the primates where a similarity existed between chimpanzees and *homo sapiens*, early speech centred on mating, food, territorial claims, pain and danger. Tribes of chimpanzees have loyalties demonstrated by extreme aggression if they encounter another tribe of apparently similar chimpanzees. Evolving chimpanzee-man with primitive speech would have advantages over others in the primary activities of mating, feeding and establishing territorial claims. Individuals of such chimpanzee-man speaking tribes who were blessed with longevity would be able to give advice to young individuals based on personal experience by giving them extra advantages over the inherited instincts alone, and in future generations an oral recorded history of the tribe would exist.

The questions 'Why are we here?, Where do we come from?' and 'Where will we go?', would eventually be asked by intelligent individuals and then the elders would need to respond. To be honest and say that we do not know would be unacceptable, the elders would 'lose face'. The obvious modes of explanations would be to relate the answers to observable mysteries, the sun, moon and stars, elusive wild animals, and the spirits of departed members of the tribe. These are the basics of all primitive religions and once a particular explanation was forthcoming, uncertainty and debate would weaken resolve and an oral creed would naturally be reinforced by explanatory images even before any written language had been developed. The ancient elaborate totem poles of North American Indian tribes in western Canada are beautiful examples of the relics of advanced early religious beliefs. Once there is an established orthodox religious belief, the stage is set for a definition of 'good' people — following the orthodox line — and 'evil' — dissenters from the orthodox. An aesthetic awareness would encourage artistic totem poles or cave paintings and attractive intonations of the creed would be the earliest examples of poetry and music.

Personality and Memory

What is meant by the personality? It is difficult to define and is sometimes identified as the essence of the person. Certainly, as far as we can tell, all conscious and unconscious sensations occur in the brain which may be regarded in some, but not all ways, as a super computer. All external stimuli of the five senses that the brain receives will go through the process of sifting according to importance. Pleasant experiences will be remembered with instant recall without any difficulty for the whole life of the individual, so will especially tragic experiences, such as the sudden loss of a loved one in an accident. Other items will be stored for recall but not easily available in memory after a period of time, for example, many of the facts that we learn at school and university. I remember a short spell in my life, of intense study of anatomy, when I could answer virtually any question that could be asked from large textbooks of anatomy. This information was useful in the examination but was over-burdening to my brain and very rapidly was dispatched to a less available 'records room'. But I know it is still there, because if I have occasion to operate on a part of the body with which I am not familiar in terms of routine surgery, I can open Gray's Anatomy and the recall is rapid, so that sometimes the actual words in the book can be remembered, occasionally even to finishing one page and knowing what will be on the top of the next. Nevertheless, if I had been asked to describe these details I would not have been able. The immediately available record library is limited but the brain probably has many subsidiary areas for storing memories. Often they come to the process of consciousness in old age or are triggered by some familiar but long-forgotten stimulus, as for example, the smell of a room from childhood, the sound of a tune not heard for many years, the sight of a painting that has been viewed in a gallery a long time back. Although the anatomy of the brain has been studied in detail, and many of the main circuits are clearly mapped out like motorways on a road map, the intricate workings of memory, consciousness, recall and the different emotions associated with feelings of envy, aggression, compassion, despair, love and hate, are not so clearly understood. They can to some extent be measured and assessed, and in any population each is distributed according to the frequency distribution bell pattern, with the proviso that, if the brain is diseased or deranged, cases will lie outside the expected range in one or more of the categories mentioned.

Early Civilisations

We can now consider human nature with the characteristics that are additional to and distinct from animals. In terms of evolutionary success, primitive men with possession of language and religion will have an advantage over chimpanzees. They will be able to plan and co-operate in hunting and fruit gathering expeditions, and the religious creed leads automatically to disciplinary measures to ensure conformity and the organisation of tribal activities. The dominant male or leader will rise to a position of authority, not only by reason of his physical prowess in fighting, but also by his ability to manipulate the behaviour of the tribe by a practical interpretation of religious creed, namely, the use of his intellect or intelligence. The leader would have the role of chieftain/priest. The development of 'shorthand' modifications of totems, and of cave paintings, led independently to written language in different, geographically separated tribes. This stage of development was the starting point for the great ancient civilisations, in Mesopotamia, Egypt, China, India and later in Greece; they all depended on the establishment of the farming of animals, the planting of crops, and residence in permanent locations, namely the formation of villages, towns and cities.

To live together in a stable community requires an increase in the complexity of rules, which are often associated with religious practices. In Ancient Egypt, sun worship and the management of the dead were all important. There was a strict separation of secular life which existed on the east bank of the Nile and the marvellous architecture, sculpture and painting, a prerogative of the priests and the dead, on the west bank. The chieftain priests or pharaohs were powerful enough to maintain discipline by developing strong armies that successfully restricted all dissent for thousands of years.

Nomadic tribes of hunters and fruit-gatherers without a written language usually follow a simple religion with a few portable 'religious' totems and relics and have special ceremonies for the celebration of birth, puberty, victory and the rituals surrounding death. The essential mobility of the tribe ensured that the sick and the aged were left behind to perish. The development of such skills as farming animals, raising crops, the use of fire to keep warm and to cook food, and the building of shelter to protect themselves from the weather and from predatory animals allowed some tribes to settle and form villages, towns and cities. With the relative respite that resulted from this stability there was time for religious views to become structured, and observed with continuity. The priestly chieftain's family formed a caste that was able to increase its power at the expense of the rest. For society to exist, certain social rules were also necessary, for example, murder, rape and theft, being anti-social, were taboo. Loyalty to the religion was essential and this loyalty implied the duty to take up arms either to defend the community from human aggressors or to plunder and conquer. When enemies were vanquished, if their lives were spared, they could be of use to the community in much the same way that farmed animals were used, taking on menial duties and making life more agreeable to the citizens.

If the rules were transgressed punishment was inflicted on the wrong-doer. This required a system of justice which even in the earliest civilisations was based on mutual tolerance, but if harm was done the criminal would be similarly harmed, 'an eye for an eye and a tooth for a tooth.' It is interesting that aggression has been a constant feature throughout history, occurring when one individual tribe clashes with another, in very much the same way as conflict results when a troop of chimpanzees meets another troop, when a pride of lions infringes another's territory, or when one clan of hyenas encounter another.

Conscience and Sense of Humour

I have suggested that good and evil have usually been defined according to creeds that have been central to all major religions. Disobeying the commandments that are associated with that creed will result in punishment if caught, but if the misdemeanour or crime is undetected, the individual, aware of what he has done, will be liable to a feeling of guilt. A guilty conscience may result from doing what is regarded as evil in one's own cultural setting but such behaviour might be quite acceptable in another. For example, there is little evidence that people were seriously conscience-stricken in all the major ancient civilisations by keeping slaves, whom they subjected to a humiliating and sometimes barbarous treatment. Pre-marital intercourse was regarded as an evil and certainly would have resulted in a guilty conscience a mere forty years ago in the West in most environments. It is still a heinous crime in many Muslim, Hindu and Catholic communities, but in the so-called 'developed' nations, pre-marital intercourse is practised by most and the institution of marriage is regarded as unnecessary by many, while up to 30% of marriages end in divorce. This has a serious effect on family loyalties: an extended family is now unusual in western nations but the lack of integrity, support, cohesion and family loyalty may be something that, although given up easily, will cause great sadness and regret later.

A sense of humour would seem to be a very human characteristic. Some animals possess behavioural characteristics that we might feel indicate humour, particularly in young animals playing with each other and with adults, but the construction of a joke or a humorous situation with the unexpected punch-line and sense of irony depend on language or abstract concepts that fit in with my previous discussions of what constitutes the essential difference between man and other higher primates.

Human Attributes

From the simple ancient historical survey that I have outlined, it is possible to look at certain characteristics of human nature to seek an explanation for some of the more complicated aspects of society that now exist. We have seen that while looking for answers to the basic questions 'Where do we come from?', 'Why are we here?' and 'Where are we going?', rational human beings have constructed religious creeds which have also been valuable to establish a hierarchy of power and a workable urban society. In general, good and evil can be defined in terms of this creed. To comply with the creed is good, the reverse is evil. Thus it is good to live in peace with one's neighbour, to obey the commands of the chieftain priest, to fight for the city state, to avoid theft, rape and murder and any subject or form of behaviour that is taboo according to the religion. Until recently, most communities followed these general dictates and found nothing evil in the concept of enslaving their vanquished foes, though there can be no doubt that the slaves themselves felt that their treatment was evil, even though the alternative of being slaughtered might be worse.

If one attempts to measure the power of human attributes, most will fit into the 'bell shaped' distribution curve. It is well known that no matter how intelligence is measured, there will always be a few brilliant individuals, some who are extremely slow-witted, and the majority will be somewhere in between. Mental disease, of course, can cause the shift of an individual usually to the left, but occasionally to the right, of the curve with behaviour that may be completely inexplicable. Fleetness of foot can similarly be measured, as can the ease with which an individual is provoked to aggressive behaviour and the intensity of that aggression. There are certain very basic human characteristics that also vary in the same manner, the capacity to love a relation or friend or one's own child, and the intense aggravation that is felt when another individual gets a reward which you feel should be yours. Envy and greed are particularly strong human characteristics, as is the sense of power and the ability to control other individuals that is associated with power. It always amazes me how otherwise pleasant, rational, and intelligent individuals are prepared to go to considerable lengths and discomfort to dress up in uncomfortable, impractical clothes, often with the heavy trimmings of metal chains of office that pull on their necks. They will then beam all evening shaking hands with people, many of whom they do not know and some they may even dislike. This usually precedes an indifferent meal served by sullen staff over a prolonged period of time. That this type of 'entertainment' is acceptable, let alone pleasurable to most people, can only be explained in terms of the celebration of pomp and power that is associated with these rituals of contemporary society.

Uniforms, badges and weapons of office, and ritual ceremonies are to be found in all ancient civilisations. Initially centred on religion they have spread into the secular domain. Laziness and lustfulness are also important human characteristics and if one tries to look dispassionately at the citizens of a town, one can see that individuals will vary widely in each of these characteristics as well. It is likely that

Figure 10. 'Expulsion of Adam and Eve from Paradise' by Masaccio from the frescoes of the Brancacci Chapel in the church of St. Maria del Carmine, Florence. Copyright © Olivetti/Electa, Italy

the intelligent, strong, crafty individuals will attain the top positions and become the priest/chieftains or equivalent, but the top man always needs to look over his shoulder since the next person in the pecking order will be not far away with a knife poised. This situation is very similar to what we observe in many mammalian societies where the dominant male is always vulnerable to his successor, usually younger and more vigorous than he is. Many of the attributes mentioned above appear to us to be unattractive, but they are very real. To look at society more favourably, we can emphasise such powerful emotions as love, compassion, charity, generosity and kindness of spirit. Some people are prepared to give all their possessions to others and sacrifice themselves for no personal gain.

In order to control these many varieties of differing human characteristics and emotions, some of which can be extremely powerful, most societies have evolved clear codes of behaviour based on guidelines and rules, transgression of which may involve a terrible punishment. Belief in the creed is usually the first and foremost rule of a code of conduct, and this is followed by the prohibition of theft, murder and rape. The Ten Commandments of ancient Israel are clear and useful examples which have stood the test of time but have also in every generation been transgressed, often by the same people who have been entrusted with priestly powers in the interpretation of the code. Evil is recorded in 'Genesis' at the very beginning of the story of creation (*figure* 10) and fratricidal murder was the first dreadful crime perpetrated by Cain, killing his brother Abel; both were sons of Adam and Eve. A similar scenario of early civilised man can be found in the history of all ancient civilisations.

Successful city states were inclined to venture beyond their own territory. Some conquests were remarkable, as when the young Alexander the Great conquered nation after nation to establish an empire stretched from Macedonia, north of Greece, to deep into the Indian sub-continent via the Middle East. The Roman Empire included most of Europe and the Middle East and extended to Britain in the north, but long lines of communication were difficult to maintain, and with poor communications local commanders in distant parts were either vulnerable to local aggression or tempted to secede from the rule of the centre. Travel was only possible by horse, foot or sailing ship. It is almost miraculous that Rome was able to maintain its empire for so long and it is not surprising that eventually the good life made possible by plunder and slave labour should corrupt those in power at the centre into lazy, soft, fat and indulgent individuals, easy prey for the hardened barbarian warrior tribes in the north and east.

I have tried to trace human nature and behaviour from the time when primitive man emerged from the apes, developing a spoken language, to the wandering tribes of hunter/fruit gatherers and then to the major changes that followed, as he acquired skills in farming animals and growing plants, developing a written language with an established religion, code of behaviour and an army. The ability to make tools and weapons, first of bronze, then of iron, resulted in extraordinary achievements of civilisations which were diverse and often magnificent. All the successful nation states utilised slavery and the elaboration of religious rituals, totems and images led to activities which we call cultural. These developed from religious roots and grew secular offshoots in literature, poetry, drama, sculpture, architecture, painting and music. Those who were successful in the hierarchy of power tended to be intelligent, active in physical combat, but were often ruthless and treacherous as well: they became tyrants. The code of practice laid down for the citizens was seldom followed by the rulers; the priests in Ancient Egypt accepted from the people on behalf of the gods some of the most delectable gifts and then appropriated them for themselves. The evolving societies developed pride and satisfaction in their achievements. Those with access to the sea explored the oceans, for acquisitive gain as well as for fishing. When foreign tribes or civilisations were encountered by the explorers, although trade and commerce was possible and sometimes occurred, combat and enslavement of the natives often followed. Civilisations waxed and waned for several thousand years until the invention of explosive gunpowder by the Chinese was harnessed to military machines by western nations. This was the beginning of the era of one-sided military advantage which has expanded from superior weapons to the mushroom cloud of an atomic blast. This progression will be considered later.

The Importance of 'Sin'

I have tried to outline the way in which *homo sapiens* differed from the higher apes. Intermediate chimpanzee-man became cleverer than the apes in developing communication by language, he was able to hunt and gather food more efficiently, and he was more successful in combat with other primate tribes that were less advanced. The origins of language are not well understood. There is a close relationship of gesture to speech, and language can also exist in written form independently of sound. The ability of man to think in abstract terms could be interpreted and communicated by a spoken language and also by gesture, so that when the questions 'Where do we come from?', 'Why we are here?' and 'Where are we going?' were asked, the most intelligent members of the tribe provided answers which involved primitive religion to which creeds and codes of behaviour were attached. The concepts of good and evil were defined by the creed, and with the acquired ability to farm animals, to plant crops and to subjugate slaves, city states were by degrees established. The chieftain-priests consolidated their power, and art forms initially based on religion, came into being. These were developed by artists and eventually appreciated by the populace so that both an ethical and an aesthetic sense and appreciation resulted from man's endeavour to answer the basic abstract questions about life. In the early religious texts the creeds and codes of behaviour were often illustrated with legends of previous chieftain-priests. The early writings of the Old Testament define a code whereby the Ten Commandments were wonderfully adapted to civilised living at the time, and in the story of the creation of man, the concepts of good, evil, temptation and murder were all introduced in understandable terms at the beginning of the Old Testament. Eve was created from Adam's rib and then succumbed to the temptation of the serpent; she disobeyed the specific instruction of God not to take the fruit from the tree of knowledge. Adam and Eve were banished from the idyllic Garden of Eden and this became the symbol of original sin and the guilt associated with it. The story's moral is that, while transgression of the creed is abhorred, these are characteristics of human nature; later, in the Book of Genesis, Cain, one of the sons of Adam and Eve, commits the first murder, which is motivated by envy when he kills his brother, Abel. With a beginning like this, it is not surprising that the history of man, both in mythology and reality, has consisted of a succession of dark and dreadful episodes, but with enlightenment and compassion present as well, the two often coexisting.

A study of the great religions shows that the patterns of worship are remarkably similar in the main religions, although the legends and the creeds in each case are different. Even when the variations between sects of the same religion appear to the outsider to be minimal, they are frequently more than sufficient cause for the most bloodthirsty wars. Supporters of one sect feel justified in sacrificing themselves for the cause and can without hesitation, and with enthusiasm, kill, rape and steal from those who espouse a slightly different interpretation of the creed.

In the name of religion many people have been killed and tortured throughout history, and this apparently mad behaviour of man is recorded in the earliest written texts and is still familiar to all of us today in current conflicts of nationality and religion throughout the world. It would seem that a cause inflamed by religious fervour will persist through generations of hatred and bigotry more than any secular reason for conflict. The recent demise of what appeared to be a highly successful secular communist creed in many countries shows how much more fundamental and important are long-sustained beliefs that are based on a religious code of ethics rather than on an agnostic, rationalist or materialist system, although, today, nationalist fervour in many parts of the world can have an intensity similar to religious fundamentalism.

The city states that were established close to the open sea developed skills in fishing and in navigating the oceans, at first close to home, but soon the more adventurous seaman, overcoming the hazards of storms and shipwreck, began increasingly to explore distant lands. Initial contact with other tribes or cities, although traditionally adversarial, was often found to be of mutual benefit by the exchange of goods without resorting to war or invasion. Trade developed by sea, along the rivers and across lakes and seas as well as over land, by nomadic tribes and trade routes by merchants. Extraordinary journeys were navigated across unfriendly terrain, menaced by dangerous predators, both animal and human, and an established trade route became an important land communication between China, the Middle East and Europe. Cities along this 'silk road' became powerful and rich due to the benefits of trade between east and west. To facilitate this trade, commercial institutions introduced money to use in the exchange of goods.

From time to time certain city states decided that a powerful armed force could produce riches more quickly and efficiently by plunder than by the slower process of building an economy on trade. A strong army and navy could invade neighbouring states, subjugate and exploit them and then use their citizens as slaves.

This was the beginning of the concept of the empire which has persisted throughout history wherever one nation state has developed a superior force. The Romans' construction of roads was probably a major factor in the prolonged success of the Roman Empire which for centuries was able to subjugate most of the known world. Victorious conquering powers usually exploit their foes as they wish, but religious coercion is difficult and perhaps impossible in far distant lands. The human resolve to maintain a religious faith has been demonstrated repeatedly by Jews, Muslims, Hindus, Buddhists and Christians. The early Christians were regarded by the official establishment in Rome as an irritating nuisance, but unlikely to have much influence on the great Roman Empire. This perception persisted until the Roman Emperor Constantine converted to Christianity. Then the boot was on the other foot. Christianity, once in power, became as intolerant as its early persecutors had been. The Spanish conversion of the Filipino nation to Christianity, to give one example, was simply and brutally accomplished by killing all those who were reluctant to accept baptism.

Citizens of conquered nations who co-operated with their imperial masters usually converted to the religion of the emperor, and the assimilation of citizens into the dominant cultures was an alternative to slavery. Great and powerful imperial nations were sufficiently rich as a result of plunder, trade and slave labour to be able to indulge in the creation of magnificent buildings and the sponsorship of artists capable of producing beautiful sculpture, drawing, painting and music. In some societies cultural pursuits remained linked to religion, in others, they mixed religious and secular cultural achievements and new rituals were established. Many primitive societies had important cultural festivals that were associated with birth, puberty, marriage and death and also erotic festivals that were linked to the harvest and fertility in man, animals and plants. Sculpture and painting tended to follow certain strict conventions: for example, the stylised attitudes of figures created in Ancient Egypt are quite different from the more realistic forms favoured by the Greeks and the Romans. In the east there were strict conventions as to the ways that religious legends could be represented in art.

Religious practices have varied enormously in history, but a strict fundamental creed has always been easier to enforce and to ensure discipline. The toleration of different views weakened faith and obedience and the unity of the community. The power of religious fundamentalism is evident throughout history and it is certainly prominent in contemporary life. Although the details of practice vary in different religions, the general principle that religion should be involved in every aspect of life is a feature of fundamentalism in all religions. Religious creeds which have a clear answer to the question 'Where are we going?', expressed in terms of heaven for the righteous and damnation for the rest, encourage a fatalistic and fanatical adherence to religion and this facilitates the recruitment of young men to fight against apparently overwhelming opposition. They know they are likely to die and are convinced that in death they will be rewarded for their valour and their adherence to the fundamental religion.

Altruism

Behavioural biologists have written extensively on the question of whether animal behaviour involves genuine altruism, defined as unselfish conduct which is often dangerous and involves sacrifices on behalf of the well-being of others. The strongest examples are a mother's love for her offspring and, to a lesser extent, the loving relationship between mates which appears to exist particularly strongly in swans that have the same faithful mating partners year after year. The question of altruism when directed towards individuals outside the family is more disputed. We have seen that killer ants will protect their nests and sacrifice themselves. Such instinctive programmed behaviour is important for the survival of a community, but whether or not this constitutes altruism, since the behaviour is pre-determined, is arguable. All living beings are constructed from the same basic building blocks of DNA and their behaviour can be regarded in a mechanistic sense as pre-determined, with their inherited instincts responsible for the manner in which they will react to the environment. Bernard Dixon[11] suggests that 'selfish genes' may

> ...account for the altruistic behaviour that is difficult to explain on Darwinian grounds. Why, for example, should worker bees, which do not even reproduce themselves, sting intruders into a hive, when they lose their lives in the act of doing so? The phrase 'selfish gene', popularised by Oxford zoologist Richard Dawkins, illuminates this issue by suggesting that we consider evolution from the point of view of the gene itself.
>
> From this perspective, cells and bodies are simply temporary vehicles to house genes and provide for their onward transmission. A selfish gene is thus concerned only with its own survival, rather than with that of the individual of which it is part. Genes may evolve in such a way that they can direct individuals to behave altruistically, benefiting other individuals carrying the same gene.

Given behaviour is governed to a large extent by the conventions and rules of society and although there is a natural, territorial and competitive side to our nature, there is also a compassionate component which may predominate. There have always been outstanding individuals who are prepared to suffer privation, hunger and danger in caring for other afflicted humans such as the monks who looked after lepers, and nurses who work in dangerous combat zones to care for the wounded. I see in my own work as a surgeon patients admitted in a critical state following illness or injury. There is usually an extraordinary rallying together of the family and at least a temporary 'burying of hatchets' that previously had often been wielded in rivalry, personal ambition or envy. The sick individual in the family becomes in a crisis the focus of their attention, and no stone will be left unturned where there might be a solution to help the stricken kinsman. The younger members

---

11 Bernard Dixon, Editor, *Medical Science Reports*

of this family might previously have been quite happy to indulge in mindless gratuitous violence at a football match, with the distinct possibility of causing injury equivalent to or worse than that from which their own relation is suffering, but at present he is the subject of their concern and compassion. It is these paradoxes of human nature that need to be considered in the context of the damage that humans are causing to other living beings and the surface of the earth.

Gunpowder to Nuclear Weapons

In the nature of things, certain aspects of human behaviour are always evolving but in the period of recorded history, at which I have looked in this brief survey, there is no evidence that human nature has changed significantly. All the characteristics that I have mentioned about ancient civilised man still exist today, but technological advances, most of which are scientifically based, have brought about many of the recent most worrying problems of man's relationship to the earth. Although the use of metal weapons, first bronze, then iron, were important military developments, the biggest change came with the invention of gunpowder by the Chinese, originally for use in fireworks, which radically altered the nature of combat previously limited to swords, spears and arrows. Death could now be administered from a distance in relative safety for those perpetrating the attack. The cannon and the musket changed warfare on land and at sea, favouring those who had these weapons. Nations that possessed the industry, and the intellectual and financial resources to devise more efficient ways of utilising explosives to kill fellow human beings had the upper hand. This enabled Christian nations in the Middle Ages to assume dominance over all others, at least until the Muslims had their own firearms. Spectacular advances were made by western countries in building and navigating ships; the bravery and fortitude of the sailors resulted in all the seas of the world being navigated, and when new land was encountered, it was usually captured and colonised, most of the natives being killed or subjugated. Especially tragic was the virtual destruction of the American Indians in both the north and southern halves of the continent, and a similar fate was meted out to the Aboriginal tribes of Australia. In Africa another shameful act was the trading and exploitation of the native population as slaves, transported to the Caribbean and America. This planted the seeds of much of the hatred that is now encountered in the inner cities of some western nations.

We can see from our consideration of human nature, the causes of the territorial and religious rival antagonisms that resulted among western Christian nations, many being almost perpetually at war with each other, while similar wars existed between Muslim nations. There were vicious crusading wars between Muslims and Christians and between the Mogul and ancient Hindu civilisations of India. The paradoxical pattern of the growth of civilisations and simultaneous uncivilised behaviour towards others continued without much major change up to the present century, when rapid scientific advances paved the way for new killing devices on a scale many times greater than anything that had been previously possible. The development of flying machines, and their refinement into accurate and deadly weapons, and above all the unleashing of the extraordinary power of the atom, changed the nature of warfare. But at the same time the increase in world population has resulted in the exploitation of the world's natural resources to an unprecedented degree. Forests are destroyed, rivers, lakes and seas are polluted, precious underground water is wasted. Greed for short-term farming profit has resulted in many arable areas becoming deserts. Unrenewable fossil-fuels are being rapidly consumed, and the carbon dioxide released into the atmosphere is probably changing the climate, causing global warming that melts the Arctic and Antarctic icecaps, and will raise the sea level and cause disastrous flooding. Modern appliances release gases that seriously deplete the ozone layer of the atmosphere, with the accompanying danger of excessive exposure to ultra-violet light. All these things are well known. In the next chapter I propose to examine some of the reasons why this rape of the earth is continuing and why very little has been done to stop it. In taxonomy, man has the presumption to label himself *homo 'sapiens'* but I think the evidence of his wisdom is lacking in the results.

The development of language and the ability to manipulate the environment define our real achievements. *Homo 'loquens et manipulans'* describe us best. *Sapiens* can be aspired to, but if things continue in the direction they seem to be going, the *sapiens* will never be reached.

Chapter 5

Science and Art

The Scientific Method

My main argument centres on the observation that the balance between man and nature has been altered to an alarming and potentially destructive extent by the application of science. The expanding human population, with its consumption of natural resources, its destruction of plants, animals and the environment and our potential ability to annihilate all life by nuclear energy, are due to the application of the extremely successful scientific approach. It is interesting to consider the highly developed ancient civilisations that achieved stability with outstanding cultural and architectural achievements without much science as it is at present understood. Although the word science means knowledge, the knowledge in modern science derives from observations that can be measured and tested. Simple, careful observations of the sun, moon and stars permitted navigation, which verified the observations. Ships were able to find their way back to port, even at night. Physical laws, relating to the space occupied by a given substance, and its weight or density, were immortalised in the story of the bath and Archimedes, who developed a simple method of water displacement to measure volume. Probably apocryphal is the story that he leaped from the bath and ran naked through the streets exclaiming 'EUREKA — I have found it.' These and other rather sporadic observations did not really constitute the birth of science, which had to wait until the Renaissance when the brilliant minds of Copernicus, Galileo, Newton and Harvey were able to deduce general principles from observations, and make prediction based on hypothesis, discovering certain natural laws which formed the beginning of science as we know it.

I will consider each of these briefly and look at their major contributions in probing accepted wisdom. To point out, with the overwhelming evidence available, that certain facts accepted by the Church and State were simply wrong, was dangerous. The scientific pioneers of the fifteenth, sixteenth and seventeenth centuries had to be very cautious, but King Charles II who was restored to the throne of England in 1660, gave his patronage to the idea of science. The social meetings of the men of science and of philosophy in coffee houses became regularised as 'The Royal Society', which still flourishes today. Charles II, encouraged science as a legitimate intellectual activity which might even benefit mankind.

Scientists were asking questions very similar to those posed by early Man. But instead of 'Where do we come from?', 'Why are we here?', 'Where are we going?', the scientists were more likely to ask 'How does it work?', 'What are the links in the chain from mating to the birth of a child?', 'What happens in a thunderstorm?', 'Why does water flow only downhill?', 'What is the composition of different materials?' In the ancient civilisations the answers to these questions would have been mystically related to man's observations of heavenly bodies, particularly of the sun and moon. Mathematics became important when goods were exchanged, and such a means of measurement developed into an essential part of daily life. Mathematics and astronomy were particularly well developed in ancient Mesopotamia, Egypt, China and, later, in Greece. The measurement of time and the seasons required a calendar and various forms of calendar were produced in each of these civilisations. Although there were important practical applications of mathematics and astronomy, the link to mysticism and religion led to untested dogma that was generally accepted in medieval Europe and could only be studied and questioned at great risk.

NICHOLAS COPERNICUS (1473-1543)

Copernicus was born and worked in Poland but visited Italy as a young man where he came in contact with the cultural and scientific stirrings of the Renaissance. The old accepted Greek theories of nature, especially the dogmas of Aristotle, had been questioned, and Leonardo da Vinci was studying human anatomy, biology, flying machines, cannons, and new methods of waging war, at the same time as he was painting some of his greatest masterpieces. This atmosphere of cultural enquiry that Copernicus found in Italy must have fired him with curiosity. When he returned to Poland, with the blessing of the Church, he set about investigating astronomy. From a careful study of the motion of the sun, the planets and the changes in the brightness of the planets, Copernicus was able to deduce the concept of the solar system, with the sun, and not the earth, as the centre. The earth and other heavenly bodies rotated on their own axes while moving in orbits around the sun. Because of the close relationship of the earth, sun and planets to each other and their lack of apparent relationship to the stars, Copernicus proposed that the solar system was but one small part of a huge universe. Needless to say these views were shocking and dreadful to those who were able to understand them. Copernicus died in 1543 and his contribution to astronomy marked the beginning of modern science. His work was continued by the German astronomer Johannes Kepler[12] who proved that the orbit of the planet Mars is an ellipse and whose studies on planetary motion paved the way for Newton's universal theory of the force of gravity.

GALILEO GALILEI (1564-1642)

An Italian who studied the stars and planets with a telescope that he developed with two lenses, Galileo was able to confirm the observations and theories of Copernicus. He proposed the law of universal acceleration for falling bodies, but his experimental demonstration of this by dropping objects of different weights from the leaning tower of Pisa may be legendary. He clashed with the Church and had publicly to recant his views since he was in grave danger of being severely punished by the

[12] Johannes Kepler 1571-1630

religious inquisition. Only in the last few years has the Church of Rome officially given a partial pardon to Galileo with an implied acceptance of his work, more than three centuries after his death.

ISSAC NEWTON (1642-1727)

Born in the year that Galileo died, Isaac Newton was the father of mathematical physics. He invented the discipline of the calculus and was able to use his brilliance in mathematics to analyse the laws of motion and mechanics and the force of gravity.[13] He did not see his work as a clash with religious doctrine and he was accepted in Cambridge where he was a scholar. He was careful to point out that all his theories fitted within a theological framework so as not to cause outrage to the Church.

WILLIAM HARVEY (1578-1657)

At the same period that these important new concepts in astronomy and mathematics were being developed, Harvey, a medical graduate of Cambridge, went to study in Padua at a time when it was the centre of excellence for anatomy and physiology. He returned to England and produced his work on the circulation of the blood which was the beginning of scientific medicine and biology. Instead of the ebb and flow of blood, back and forth, which was the theory that had been handed down from the time of Aristotle, Harvey proved that blood must move from the arteries to the veins via minute vessels, the capillaries. These could not at that time be visualised, rather like Mendel's demonstration of the laws of heredity where invisible genes and chromosomes were deduced by hypothesis.

The invention of the microscope, together with the telescope, permitted detailed study of small structures and of distant heavenly bodies that had previously not been possible. In 1674 Antonie van Leeuwewhoek in Holland produced a magnifying glass that enabled him to see bacteria. An important refinement was the development of the compound microscope by Joseph Jackson Lister in 1830[14] who described with the aid of his microscope, the form of the red blood cells. Scientists frequently met together in the nineteenth century, forming societies which debated their theories and published their results. An understanding of the behaviour of liquids and gases when heated and cooled, and the combustion of materials by fire through the consumption of oxygen, heralded new ideas in the development of physics and chemistry.

[13] Newton's laws of motion are:
1. A body remains in a state of rest unless it is compelled to change by a force.
2. The change of motion of a body is proportional to the force on it.
3. To every action there is an equal and opposite reaction.

[14] Father of Joseph Lister, the surgeon.

The Technological Exploitation of Science

The history of science outlined above did little to change the way people lived until the application of this knowledge, and such methods of observation and experimentation, were introduced into industry, travel and medicine. The invention of the condensing steam-piston engine in 1764 by James Watt was used in industry, and developed by Richard Trevithiek in 1803 to power a locomotive. This was the beginning of modern travel. The early steam engine was followed, in succession, by the invention of the internal combustion diesel and petrol engines, the rotating steam turbine, and the internal combustion turbine of the jet engine. The jet engine has revolutionised travel and the means of making war. An understanding of electricity and magnetism was fundamental to these developments, as were new experimental chemical investigations, and the theory of elements and of chemical reactions. All these scientific observations and the inventions they brought into being could now be utilised in commercial ventures in industry and in warfare. The industrial revolution changed forever the pattern of living in western nations and in North America.

Biology and medicine lagged behind the growth of engineering and technology and they necessarily depended on the utilisation of physics and chemistry to understand the mechanisms of living matter, especially disease and the way in which disease disturbs the body, as well as the causes of disease and finding new strategies for curing illness. The most important development in the context of human population was the introduction of vaccination against smallpox by Jenner in 1796. He observed that milk girls contracting a mild pox disease from cows became resistant to the devastating scourge of smallpox. Jenner was then able to show that by deliberately inoculating the cow pox serum into uninfected people it was possible to protect them from infection with smallpox. This was the beginning of preventative vaccination, and smallpox has now been eliminated as a disease. Routine vaccination can prevent epidemics of diphtheria, measles, poliomyelitis and tetanus, all previously common fatal diseases. At the same time an understanding of the relationship of dirt and poor sanitation to many diseases, particularly cholera and typhoid, made it possible to prescribe fairly straightforward measures of hygiene to prevent these diseases. Louis Pasteur[15] disproved the theory of spontaneous generation, by heating or 'pasteurisation' which killed bacteria. He prevented harmful fermentation in the production of wine. The surgeon Joseph Lister[16] introduced antisepsis into surgery, thereby transforming an extremely dangerous form of treatment into routine therapy. Semmelweis[17] independently showed that the common fatal infection of mothers after childbirth could be prevented if the attending doctors and nurses washed their hands in antiseptic solution. The other great advance in medicine was the introduction of antibiotics,

[15] Louis Pasteur, French scientist 1822-1895
[16] Joseph Lister, English surgeon 1827-1912
[17] Ignaz Phillipp Semmelweis, Hungarian, 1818-1865

so that many diseases that used to be fatal, such as pneumonia, osteomyelitis and tuberculosis could be treated successfully.

Contemporary Medicine Application of the Scientific Method

Science has transformed medicine from a mystical, ineffective and often harmful profession to a powerful and successful calling in the prevention and treatment of disease. The scientific method of assessment should be routine in medicine, but even today this is not always the case. If a new antibiotic was thought, from scientific laboratory experiments, capable of killing the AIDS or the rabies virus, then the trial of this antibiotic in full-blown AIDS patients or those who have developed symptoms of rabies, would quickly show whether the hopes based on laboratory experiments would be fulfilled in man. If any of the patients survived, this would be very strong evidence in favour of the efficacy of the antibiotic, since no patient has ever previously survived either of these diseases.

It becomes more difficult to investigate new cures for disease where there are different effective treatments available. Failure to use the scientific method leads to uncertainty and confusion; for example, in the surgery for gallstones, the usual treatment is removal of the gall bladder through an incision 10 cms long, and recovery takes a week to ten days. A new form of operation, 'keyhole' or laparoscopic surgery, enables the gall bladder to be removed through several very small incisions while the surgeon manipulates the instruments guided by a picture on a television screen. The recovery period from this operation is a matter of two or three days with much less pain. There are, however, certain risks with the keyhole technique because the surgeon is restricted to a two-dimensional view instead of three-dimensions in the normal operation. To investigate all the pros and cons of the new technique in a scientific manner would require a carefully controlled study, comparing the two techniques with very strict supervision and monitoring to hold back the natural enthusiasm and bias that tend to be attached to a new treatment. To date, such a randomised, controlled, statistically-assessed trial has not been done, but the media reports have been exceedingly positive and a whole new surgical instruments industry has been developed. Most patients are very pleased with the new operation. This is no comfort to the poor patient who has suffered a severe complication or even worse, or for the relatives of the patient who dies from a complication, so it is important to determine if the incidence of serious complication is greater with the new technique. We also need to know if the good results of the technique in experienced hands can be duplicated by surgeons in the process of learning the new technique. These are the kind of questions that are central in developing new forms of treatment. We can be prevented from getting a satisfactory answer by too much media 'hype' and over-enthusiastic initial bias in favour of the new technique, which inhibits doctors from taking part in the type of scientific trial that should be done. The advocates of the new treatment say that a trial would be unethical, but for a potential patient it is important to know whether treatment A although less painful, has twice the mortality of treatment B.

Another example, which I call the 'Dark Disco syndrome', is commonly encountered when a new promising drug is first investigated. The early experimental results and observations of the effects on patients are viewed, quite unintentionally, with a marked bias. The reason is probably the immense amount of work, discussion, trial and error that has led to the clinical studies being undertaken, and the investigators can see only the good results because they want to see them. Any side effect is blinkered out of their field of vision. Time and again the evolution is similar to the initial encounter of two people in a dark disco, with minimal light and perhaps accompanying alcohol accentuating their perception of each other's charms, so that a powerful attraction ensues. When they meet again the next day in the sunshine without the environment of the dark disco the all too obvious blemishes suddenly appear and defects become apparent. The same is true with the assessment of virtually every new drug. A carefully monitored randomised trial is essential to avoid disappointment when the gloss of the initial enthusiasm has worn off and the true qualities of the drug, good and bad, are revealed. One should always be cautious and critical whenever revelations of a 'miracle' drug occupy large headlines in newspapers before the side effects have been investigated.

The Doctor's Dilemma

The traditional teaching of the medical profession requires a doctor to do everything legitimate in his power to try to help his patient. This is the Hippocratic ethos of medicine and the best possible treatment must be given irrespective of whether or not the doctor likes the patient or considers him or her feckless, ill because of self inflicted disease or injury, or a confirmed and even vicious criminal. In our contemporary market economy, with new very expensive 'high-tech' medicine and surgery, doctors are repeatedly being reminded by those responsible for managing health care that the funds available are limited and the best treatment cannot be available to all.

Since the purse for therapeutic medicine contains a finite sum, how can this best be used for the treatment of the patient in pain, frightened and disabled, and at the same time such that the decision can be judged correct by fellow citizens? Clearly there must be rationing and the solution adopted by the US State of Oregon has much to commend it, since the medical profession, the government and the 'man in the street' all have a say in the decisions.

There has been debate in the UK recently as to whether the benefits of expensive heart surgery should be freely available to recalcitrant smokers, or liver transplantation for unreformed alcoholics. This type of argument is dangerous. In what category would we place a youth who has stolen a car and injured himself? Would the assessment change if in the course of the accident he had killed a child waiting on the pavement for the school bus? How do we feel about those injured in sport? Is there a clear difference between an injury sustained playing football and one incurred during hang-gliding or bungee jumping — the latter both regarded by many as dangerous or even reckless pursuits?

In my own speciality of organ grafting there can be discussion as to whether this high-tech expensive treatment should be equally available to a severely mentally-damaged child, and a brilliant university scholar? How would we feel about the aged Michaelangelo if he needed a liver transplant? Should the stage he had reached in his painting of the ceiling of the Sistine Chapel be a consideration? Would his candidacy for a new liver be stronger if he still had half to complete? To refuse him at this stage would rob civilisation of one of its greatest artistic treasures, but if he had just finished his work and retired from painting, would the case be different? I ask these questions not because I have clear answers, but to demonstrate that the subject of medical ethics and the distribution of health care resources is complex and that each case deserves to be considered on its own merits. Whatever the decision taken on expensive treatment, the doctor still must act with compassion to comfort the sick and relieve pain.

Travel and Communication

Together with mass travel, there have been developments in mass communication, especially the telephone, with fax and satellite television now traversing the whole world. An atrocity committed in a remote region can now be viewed in the homes of peoples of every nation, as also can gratuitous violence, both fictional and real. The tools that can manipulate the minds of human beings are equally powerful in their effect on the masses of modern cities as they previously were for the much smaller communities of city states where the priest-king ruled and controlled society. The astounding modern advances in physics and mathematics that have sent satellites for communication and surveillance orbiting the world, have allowed men to visit the moon, and machines to photograph planets at relatively close distances.

Nuclear Energy

The increasingly advanced methods for studying matter in this century have led, first to an understanding of the structure of atoms and then to a dissection of that structure. Splitting the atom released frighteningly huge and potentially destructive amounts of energy that have led to the most terrible of all weapons, the nuclear bomb. The small prototype was nevertheless a weapon of mass destruction of unprecedented killing power. Now thousands of nuclear weapons of much greater death-dealing potential are stockpiled by the most powerful nations of the world. As the physicists study smaller and smaller particles of matter, they are faced with increasing uncertainty as to whether there is a boundary between matter, energy, space and time. This is a chastening thought when one looks back to the original questions, 'Where do we come from?', 'Why are we here?', and 'Where are we going?'. The answers to these questions seem to be no nearer today than they were when first asked by primitive man.

Molecular Biology

Biology is still going through a phase of rapid expansion in its exact knowledge of how things work. The DNA genome that constitutes the basis of inheritance is being unravelled and the structure of DNA itself is becoming understood in great detail. The constellations of DNA that form genes tend to move as entities and they explain many aspects of inheritance. Changes in the genes that apparently occur spontaneously, or that originate from outside causes, such as x-rays and drugs, have also been observed. The way in which the DNA produces the proteins which form the life matter of the cell and body is now understood, at least in principle. By analogy one could imagine the DNA as the metal type on an old-fashioned typewriter, limited in number to the alphabet and a few symbols, but the potential arrangement is almost without limit in terms of the message that can be conveyed when this metal die causes ink to appear on the paper. So by analogy the writing would be the proteins, as varied as a Shakespearean sonnet at one extreme, to a bureaucratic instruction from the EEC on the export of eggs at the other. In terms of proteins it could vary from an enzyme essential to digestion, involving a great deal of chemical activity, to an inert structural protein, forming the ligaments that hold a joint together. This understanding of the basic building elements of life has already allowed biologists to manipulate the genome, artificially inserting or substituting extraneous genes for the ones naturally present and producing new forms of living organisms which are called 'transgenic' individuals. The potential of these developments is not yet known but new knowledge and techniques in this area would suggest that there are many possible applications for the treatment of disease, the production of food and also no doubt there will be uses that could be harmful to man, animals and the environment.

The purpose of this chapter is to show that curious scientists interested in how things work discovered facts that challenged ancient dogma. The validity of the scientific method has been verified repeatedly by successful prediction, but scientists recognise that their knowledge is at present minimal and in every branch of science there are areas of uncertainty which are the most interesting subjects to study. The first step is to observe phenomena, and then construct an hypothesis suggesting what mechanisms might be involved, and plan and conduct experiments to determine whether the hypothesis is true or false. If true, then predictions based on the hypothesis will have repeated validity. The power and the veracity of 'the scientific method', can be seen in all aspects of everyday modern life, from the television set and the telephone to jet travel.

New forms of scientific medical treatment have upset the balance of our programmed fertility, which is far in excess of the new status quo in terms of death control; but we have dreadful new machines of war and means of distributing death. The maintenance of peace, and the restoration of the balance of population and the environment, should be governed by logic, reason and compassion rather than prejudice and greed. The spectrum of human nature is wide ranging and it is probable that love, compassion and a will to live and let live, with fellow men and animals, plants and the environment, is the wish of the majority of human beings. We must however be vigilant that a dangerous minority might overwhelm the majority view. If there is mass unemployment, terrible inequality, starvation and over-population, the veneer of civilisation can be removed and like a lethal plague, the minority with destructive hatred, and no pity, might destroy a community. It is necessary to be aware of this possibility, and harness science and scientists to solve the problems that have arisen because of the applications of science.

Art

The unique human attribute that can appreciate art and create it has ramifications in basic behavioural characteristics. I have suggested that art was derived from religious and mystical origins and is fundamentally sympathetic to the strongest instinctive biological forces: the dance of sexual courtship, the menacing dances of combat and of hunting, and the creation of images that have sacred superstitious meaning, such as warding off the 'evil eye', the worship of and respect for heroes, ancestors and gods. The rhythm of the dance is naturally accentuated by the beat of drums and enhanced by voice accompaniment. The images of totems, adorned with colour and original lines and shapes can be seen in all ancient cultures, but they soared to wondrous heights in ancient Greece. The abstract concepts required to appreciate art are instinctive, but as art forms increase in complexity and secularisation, so the paraphernalia of academic art studies became linked to a market.

The Commercialisation of Art

Some prominent critics have evolved themselves into a mafia-like conspiratorial organisation that now instructs the public on the quality and value of 'art' much of which is incomprehensible to the majority of intelligent sensitive people. Like the ancient priests, these avant-garde authorities expound to the multitude on the interpretation of huge canvases of coloured squares or spilled paint, on the chaotic arrangement of commonplace and often revolting objects, that are scarcely recognisable as belonging to the discipline of sculpture, and on the dissonant cacophony of dreadful noise that gives pleasure only when it ceases. These extremes are often highly praised and receive prestigious and valuable prizes at solemn media ceremonies that resemble farce. How can this fraudulent edifice fool so many people for so long? I suspect that most people take the modern art priests at their word and feel that their own lack of comprehension is a personal weakness, and this line of thought is of course encouraged by the 'art mafia'. There is also a major financial side to this sad story. Works of art approved by the critics can be used as investment bonds by rich entrepreneurs, and as with most other monetary bonds, their intrinsic beauty is irrelevant, it's the money that counts! Moreover, to display such objects endows the owner with a certificate of approval by the 'mafia' and helps to ensure a good profit when they fall into the hands of the next art investment millionaire.

Meanwhile the public goes its own way, mystified and divorced from an incomprehensible world of 'high' art, but happy to engage enthusiastically in other art forms. The adulation of modern 'pop stars' of music and dance is close to the religious fervour of fundamentalist regimes. The 'saint' is mobbed by the masses, and his personal artefacts are prized and revered. Pop concerts have much in common in appearance with revivalist religious congregations. Some orthodox religious leaders have even adopted pop culture to reinforce flagging religious practice, and often this brings people back to the churches, but this type of religion may not restore the discipline that is part of most successful creeds. Mysticism and fear are needed to strengthen the cohesion of all fundamentalist creeds and to depart from these principles is perilous: a religious liturgy, recited in medieval Latin incomprehensible to most of the congregation, has great force, especially if it is accompanied in the vernacular by detailed explanations of the dreadful things in the after-life that will befall those who fail to adhere to the articles of faith.

Although the enthusiasm shown is overtly less extreme than that exhibited at pop concerts, there is a strong following for 'conventional' fine art and classical music. An exhibition of renaissance or impressionist paintings will be visited by millions in any large western city, and concerts of music by Mozart, Beethoven and Mahler, and operas by Puccini and Verdi will have no empty seats.

The apologists for the current 'art mafia' point out that Van Gogh, and Schubert, and many other creative artists, had little recognition in their lifetimes. Van Gogh sold only one painting, but the art critics as well as the public failed to notice the strength and enormous originality in the works of this seriously disturbed mind. Many of the greatest artists were appreciated by their contemporaries, Michaelangelo, Leonardo da Vinci, Raphael, Rembrandt, Rubens, El Greco, Goya, and Velasquez were all successful in worldly terms. In literature Shakespeare, the greatest commentator on the human condition of all time, was a popular playwright and Mozart enjoyed adulation for much of his life, but little financial success.

The Motivation of Scientific Enquiry

Cultural pursuits are important in any consideration of human interactions, and they can trigger off powerful emotions that can influence and lead to fateful and fatalistic actions. So how does science in its widest sense fit into the human mosaic? The central characteristic of science, and the motivation of all great scientists, is an insatiable curiosity to discover, to know 'how does it work?' How do animals and plants live together? What determines the changes in climate and daily weather? What is the cause of this disease? How can we cure it? Is the hunt to discover the answer to such questions a sufficient motivation for the scientists? I suspect that it is, because Copernicus, Galileo, Newton, Darwin, Madame Curie, Rutherford and Einstein were all driven by curiosity.

The satisfaction that is derived from successful scientific enquiry is important but so also is the associated kudos that follows acceptance of the data by other scientists. The race to be first to discover the answer to a crucial question can disturb the traditional integrity of science. There are particularly powerful stimuli to be the first in a new scientific discovery, and the rewards of prestigious prizes are not only their monetary value, but also the fame that accompanies them.

The success of the western nations largely derives from their application of science to society and industry, and the most successful countries have always put the greatest investment into education in general, and science in particular. The United States of America, Germany and Japan devote major resource towards funding both basic and applied science. Pharmaceutical, manufacturing and engineering multinational companies similarly spend large sums on research and development, which pay off in new drugs, better cars, aeroplanes, communication processes, biotechnology and sources of fuel, all of which mean profit. The science of industry is naturally secretive. Discoveries must be protectively patented to prevent competitors benefiting from the money spent by the innovating companies. Industrial espionage — the stealing of secrets before they are patented, and the violation or circumvention of patents — are major worries. Not surprisingly, 'pure' academic science, as practised in universities and national research institutions, is also vulnerable to corruption. Much of modern science requires large teams working with very expensive apparatus; the decoding of the human genome is an example of a 'megascience' undertaking. Unravelling a gene sequence, with potential commercial value, and the discovery of a virus that is the cause of a dreaded disease will certainly be rewarded by major prizes: 'scientific riches' that may be exploited by the unscrupulous. Fraudulent claims of priority have corrupted scientists in the past and will probably be more common in future as the potential rewards increase. With large teams interacting on a project, individual original ideas may emanate from junior team members who may be excluded from the laurels awarded for the fruits of their originality; yet the ambience in which their ideas were able to flourish may have depended on the personal attributes and fund attracting capabilities of the team leader. These matters are worrying for those who believe that intellectual curiosity and the integrity of pure science are its most attractive characteristics, and are mainly responsible for the major successes of the past. The driving forces should be for satisfaction and achievement, but antagonisms, jealousies and corrupt behaviour, which are part of human nature, figure in both the arts and the sciences and sully the good name and honour of what should be the driving force of human progress.

Chapter 6

The Rape of the Earth and the Journey towards Self-Destruction —
The Rudderless Super Tanker Heading for the Rocks

The instinctive behaviour of primitive man, once modified by farming and the development of city states, did not greatly interfere with the ecology of other living creatures, at least not in the context of the earth's resources. It has been postulated that mammoths were exterminated by spear-wielding North American Indians and other species may well have been eliminated by early man. A visitor to the Galapagos Islands is amazed by the naturally tame disposition of many creatures not disturbed by close proximity to humans, because humans had not been a danger to them over a long enough period for them to evolve an effective evading action. Common and beautiful fishing birds living in the Galapagos were nicknamed the 'boobies' because sailors thought the birds were so stupid that they allowed humans to walk up to them and kill them. The poor 'booby' was not stupid but had just not had the experience to know how to protect itself from the marauding human. Fortunately humans now protect the 'boobies' in the Galapagos from the danger of predatory man, but the wildlife is in danger from feral rats, cats, rabbits and goats introduced to the Galapagos Islands by man.

The paradoxes of human nature, the organisation of society, the power of religious belief and the fanaticism that is associated with fundamental religion, are all important facilitators of the apparently unstoppable increase of the world population, particularly in developing countries. Following the industrial revolution, better food supplies, improved housing, later marriage, the provision of clean water and the hygienic disposal of sewage, changed the living conditions of urban populations more than the application of modern preventative medicine. In affluent, developed nations, pressures to increase the population seem to have ceased. In Europe, Italy, a catholic country, has the lowest birth-rate. The pursuit of materialistic success and the emancipation of women by the simple addition of two incomes to a family rather than one, mean that the encumbrances of large families have become unfashionable, and in some nations the population is even falling. Male and female fertility may have diminished in western nations, but while the cause is not known, one suspects that for women it is the contraceptive 'pill'. Low sperm counts in men may well be a result of oestrogen-like additives to food.

Few are starving in the prosperous nations, but there are nevertheless serious social worries. Most large cities have increasing numbers of under-privileged citizens who constitute a menacing underclass, mostly out of work, envious of the riches of the rest of the community and often prepared to resort to crime in order to improve their subsistence income provided by the state. Social volcanoes waiting to erupt exist in both poor and rich nations, wherever there is a wide gap between the poor under-privileged masses and the minority of rich. Japan, Switzerland and Singapore might appear to be relatively safe, but most other nations have disadvantaged resentful citizens whose threshold of explosive eruption would be lowered by famine, drugs or competition from new immigrants.

The natural tendency of the discontented to resort to violence has been considered in a biological, evolutionary context. Anyone who would claim that civilised man is different, should pause to observe the almost continuous outpouring of degrading violence put out as entertainment on the television screens of developed nations. It has been suggested that the portrayal of 'real life' obscene violence, shown world-wide, should serve as a caution to autocratic regimes warning them against perpetrating social injustice. I hope that this theory is true, but if the major public appetite is for fictional shooting and torture, their occurrence in reality may not seem to be so awful. The underclass is fertile ground for exploitation with drugs, and easily lured into crime, and in times of natural disaster, such as an earthquake or a hurricane, looting and widespread street violence can erupt, spreading widely from the underclass to all strata of the community, demonstrating that the veneer of civilisation is remarkably thin. During the oil crisis in North America, violence and the use of firearms were involved in the acquisition of gasoline to get ahead of other people whose cars needed replenishment. Even without conflict with the developing world, the developed nations should be far from confident that their own, isolated, affluent societies, trying to maintain law and order and a civilised, cultured existence, can continue for long. In the United States of America there is a violent death every fifteen seconds.[18]

The population in the developing world is growing at an alarming rate, especially in rural areas where extra children mean more hands to help with the labour and are a source of insurance for care when the parents get old, provided the family unit is maintained. In some communities a male offspring is far more important than a female one and the infanticide of new-born baby girls is still practised. Rural populations become demographically entrapped if they can no longer support themselves and have nowhere better to go. The people either migrate in misery to urban slums or die where they are of famine.[19] Cities in the under-developed countries usually have, for the most part, a small population of rich upper and upper-middle class citizens and a large population of lower and underclass citizens. This is an unstable mix, and the tension is demonstrated repeatedly whenever there is a chance for social unrest, often triggered by religious fundamentalism which tends to flourish best where there is widespread poverty. There have been many well-intentioned and enthusiastic efforts to control the population by voluntary methods and there has been some successes with mechanical and chemical contraceptive agents. The 'Pill' and variants of it are now available in many poor countries but their impact on population increase has been disappointing. In China, with a totalitarian regime, strict control of family numbers and the enforcement of abortions for those who defy instructions have been partly successful, but even in China the population is increasing at an unacceptable rate. Inevitably, the increased numbers mean more poverty, more exploitation of the environment, more killing of wild animals, destruction of forests, and removal of all living matter from the seas.

[18] Joycelyn Elders, *The Lancet* 1994 vol. 343 p. 40
[19] Maurice King and Charles Elliot, *The Lancet* 1993, 341, 669

The need for energy to manufacture goods means that in all countries, where fossil-fuels are available, they are being consumed without renewal. Nuclear energy, which seemed such a wonderful advance, has the potential for deadly catastrophe if strict operating rules are not followed as happened in the Chernobyl disaster. Hydro-electric energy is relatively clean and less damaging to the environment than the use of fossil fuels but huge dams change the ecology of the river valley and can be harmful. There are hopes for harnessing the power of the wind, the sun's rays, the waves of the ocean, and the tides, and of obtaining heat from volcanic sources to provide more energy that will not severely damage the planet. These approaches have not so far made a major impact on the use of irreplaceable resources. The increase in arable farming destroys forests and many plant and animal species. Huge herds of cattle produce methane which aggravates global warming.

There is nothing new in this depressing list of things that are happening: at the environmental world meeting in Rio de Janeiro in 1992 they were all discussed, but the religious lobby against birth control prevented any effective resolutions being adopted which in a global manner would control population. Individual greed, corruption, envy and exploitation made all the good resolutions impotent and avarice and materialism triumphed.

There is evidence that intelligent men and women throughout the world are aware of these matters and scientists have frequently pointed out the dangers in quantitative terms. Most politicians ignore and avoid nettles that if grasped might offend religious beliefs or interfere with their own personal chances of re-election. Long-term planning is almost non-existent in democratic countries where elections are held every three to five years and in non-democratic regimes the maintenance of the status quo by the ruling classes seems to take up most of the energies of the politicians, who look questionably at what has happened to countries where, in the name of freedom and democracy, free speech and multiple political parties have been permitted. The previously communist nations have been consumed with internecine conflict arising from religious and/or ethnic demarcations. It is hard not to believe, that with so many fanatical individuals in power or trying to achieve it, and whole nations obsessed with persistent and vengeful hatred, that the most destructive weapons available will not be used. Nuclear conflict, and the use of biological and chemical warfare would seem to be an inevitable consequence of human nature in our contemporary, highly technological age with its ever-increasing population, and in-built political systems that are incapable of long-term planning.

The rich and despotic regime of ancient Rome became a target for destruction and for plunder by the fierce 'barbarians', and so too have all civilisations that favour cruel, over-indulged ruling classes that profit from the work of slaves and the under-privileged classes. In Western democracy the social benefits that are available to citizens are attractive goals for immigrants from poorer nations. They see the sick and the unemployed tolerably well cared-for and even violent criminals treated leniently. But if they try to enter rich countries as economic refugees they are unlikely to be received generously by the poor of the democratic welfare states. The so-called 'guest-workers' from Turkey are now finding themselves unwelcome in Germany and have been subjected to brutal violence. To a greater or lesser extent guest-workers and immigrants are badly received and treated in all European countries.

The medical advances that most people would regard as laudable are responsible for the low maternal and infant death rate but there has been no serious effort to balance this lack of death control with birth control. Instead, wars, pestilence and starvation seem to be the most likely way in which population numbers will be controlled in the future. The fact that there has not been an atomic conflict since the Second World War has encouraged many to believe that 'deterrence' has preserved peace and that the threat of atomic weapons is a thing of the past. The evidence of this in the past fifty years would seem to be strong, but unfortunately the splitting of the world into affluent and poor communities with the rich having more than enough and the poor facing starvation is a serious threat. Often weaponry is all that the poor countries possess.

We know that religious and ethnic fanaticism make the personal sacrifice of life readily acceptable to minority terrorist organisations. The science and technology that is required to construct nuclear, biological and chemical weapons are well known and it is not too difficult for determined fanatical individuals to construct or buy such weapons. We all hope that the good-natured human attributes of tolerance, love and compassion will prevail, but I doubt if an optimistic view is justified unless the same scientific approach that has led to the present state of affairs can be harnessed to control the size of the human population. It is my hope that the application of science and technology can fix a rudder to the out-of-control tanker just in time. So far, however, the warnings of serious scientists have all been ignored and there is little comprehension by most of the citizens of democratic countries of the present dangers. There is an urgent need for much more public understanding, and for politicians to realise that even their short-term goals may never be fulfilled, unless they make stemming the population increase the major item of their political agendas, and seek ways and means by which this can be achieved. Control of the population is the *first* and most urgent requirement needed to maintain the civilised coexistence of a 'live and let live' philosophy between human beings.

Chapter 7

New Killing Technology

The three new techniques for killing human beings and other living creatures are chemical, bacterial and viral, and nuclear weapons.

Chemical

There are a number of poisons that have been used in warfare, and the most well known are gases, particularly chlorine and mustard gas, used during the 1914-18 World War. The effects of these agents are extremely unpleasant before they kill, and can produce long-standing morbidity, especially lung damage for the initial survivors. However, they are not especially effective as mass lethal weapons because of the difficulties of distribution. They tend to require high concentrations locally to be effective and if the wind changes they can rebound on those who released them. The toxin of ptomaine poisoning is an agent that is lethal in minute quantities. More to be feared are the recently developed neuro-toxins which in very small amounts can cause paralysis. Details of these agents are still secret but by distribution in water supplies, dreadful carnage could be wrought. The effect of most of these agents is to kill by paralysing the breathing muscles. Again there is a difficulty in distribution for really mass deadly effects.

Bacterial and Viral

Certain bacteria have been developed as weapons, for example the anthrax bacterium, which can cause a lethal infection. In the past, armies have been vanquished as a result of illness and often this has taken the form of dysentery, so deliberate contamination of water supplies with dysenteric organisms and the bacilli that cause cholera and typhoid might also be used as weapons. Antibiotics and vaccination precautions can be used to combat most bacterial infection. Viruses are more difficult to treat but also difficult to handle as weapons. The influenza, AIDS, hepatitis, and rabies viruses could all cause widespread disease and death, but at present distribution is again a difficulty in targeting such lethal infections.

Nuclear Weapons

It is here that Man has achieved a pinnacle from which to destroy all living creatures on the earth and in the sea. I have visited both Hiroshima and Nagasaki, where the first and only atom bombs have been dropped as weapons. These by modern standards were minute prototypes but the devastation caused was difficult to comprehend. At considerable distances from the epicentre, human beings were instantaneously transformed into shadows on stone, their whole bodies having been consumed and turned into gas by the extreme heat of the explosion. Those killed immediately were presumably lucky compared with those who suffered severe radiation and died terrible deaths in the ensuing weeks and months. Lethal radioactive gas hovered over the area and in each city more than 100,000 people died as a direct effect of these small nuclear bombs.

The accident at the nuclear power plant in Chernobyl showed how, when control of the mechanism of a nuclear power station was lost, a rapid build-up of explosive nuclear material could kill everybody nearby and cause extremely serious radiation damage to people and creatures over long distances, and even continents away.

These are the well-known examples of nuclear radiation that have killed and injured humans and other creatures. In context, they are almost irrelevant when one considers that the United States of America and Russia have each stockpiled more than 10,000 weapons, many of which are thousands of times more powerful than the two dropped in Japan. If even a fraction of these weapons were to explode, it is unlikely that any mammals would survive and most other creatures would suffer terrible damage. The world would be uninhabitable to all but the lowest of living matter and presumably then the whole process of evolution would have to begin again.

The Risks of a Nuclear Catastrophe

Optimists would argue that the dangers of a nuclear war are minimal in the hands of rational people and one might hope that this would be the case, but even under the most careful control, there is always a danger of human error and the compounding of abuses of fail-safe mechanisms. Already there are several instances of near catastrophes quoted, since to be of any deterrent value the weapons have to be easily armed and despatched. I think it is miraculous that a more serious accident has not so far occurred. With all the care that is taken to prevent disasters in aeroplanes, ships and trains, and with all the modern radar and navigational devices, we still witness regular catastrophes in these forms of travel. The rough balance between the nuclear threats of the west and the east has now suddenly changed. The eastern threat has disintegrated. Many of the highly paid experts in nuclear physics in Russia are now facing unemployment, their status has fallen together with their income and the same is true of the military organisation, which has been trained to use these weapons. The susceptibility to corruption amongst human beings almost certainly fits into a bell distribution curve, and like all other human characteristics, there are bound to be some individuals in possession of the knowledge, apparatus and expertise of nuclear weaponry who are corruptible, and would sell their expertise and hardware to an unprincipled buyer. There are likely to be one or two individuals in possession of nuclear weapons who have unbalanced minds. If such a corruptible mind was in contact with the leader of a military-inspired dictatorship, especially if the regime rests on some form of fundamentalist or fatalistic creed, then the stage would be set for catastrophe.

It is very likely that the acquisition of weapons of this nature by a maniacal dictator would initially be specifically targeted. Military strategists have looked carefully at this scenario and investigated ways and means by which nuclear war could be localised and contained. I have grave doubts that this would be possible. Having seen what small nuclear bombs did in Japan, the use of a modern mega-weapon in any part of the world would cause so much damage to the whole planet that it is very likely that in desperation there would be retaliation from the huge arsenals of the west, once the veneer of rational civilised behaviour had been stripped away by the catastrophic tragedy of the first nuclear attack.

The use of nuclear weapons might occur without the expected increase in population, but extreme social, national and religious pressures will all be aggravated by such an increase, bringing with it massive poverty and despair, with the danger that the misery and hatred will boil over into uncontrolled and suicidal fanaticism.

We must accept human nature because of our DNA, whether we like it or not. Aggressive behaviour, and actions that would be regarded by the majority as demented and irrational, need to be guarded against. Unfortunately the mechanisms for control have not in the past been particularly successful. Throughout history there have been notable examples of aggressive maniacal leaders, totally supported by their subjects, where loyalty is reinforced by effective propaganda, who can rally the masses to the causes of religious fundamentalism and nationalism.

A peaceful nation attacked by a fanatical aggressor with nuclear weapons would seek to retaliate with nuclear weapons if they were available. Alternatively, faced with inevitable nuclear attack, they might deliver pre-emptive strikes. I therefore see an extreme danger in the combination of political opportunism, greedy and corrupt criminal organisations, and fanatical 'freedom fighters' into a highly combustive mixture, which from a consideration of historical precedents, is likely to be sinister and violent. The greatest danger might come from an unexpected quarter with a sudden strike before there was sufficient time for international agencies, such as the United Nations, to prevent the explosion. There is an inevitable slowness in the mobilisation to action of the United Nations, which has in any case great difficulty in reaching resolutions because of the need for consensus. The initial reactive policing of the UN has in the past been taken over by a few nations, in particular the United States of America, as was exemplified recently in the Gulf War. In this conflict, the accuracy of the new weaponry in killing by conventional means was awesome.

Our predecessors established facts mainly by observation: and it was clear to them that the earth was flat, apart from mountains and valleys, and that the sun rotated around the earth once a day. These 'facts' were seen as obvious. When more careful observation and mathematical assessment showed that the earth rotated round the sun and itself rotated, explaining day and night and the seasons of the year, the astronomers were condemned as heretics and some were persecuted. Even circumnavigating the globe did not persuade the 'flat earthers' that in fact the earth was a sphere. The argument that most human beings are rational, sensible and do not wish to destroy life on earth in no way negates the alternative proposition that a few irrational, fanatical human beings would be quite prepared to destroy life on earth for the sake of their beliefs. How can the majority view be upheld? The facts posed by the nuclear threat and by human nature are established, but facts are often ignored.

Chapter 8

Can Political Regimes Respond to the Dangers?

The paradox of religion and secular liberalism is that excessive freedom leads inexorably to anarchy, and religious fundamentalism opposed to birth control results in population increase, with the danger of holy war and eventual anarchy.

A crucial question of this book is whether it is possible to reconcile human nature, dependent as it is on the DNA we receive from our parents, with a peaceful coexistence with the rest of the planet. Looking back at history and viewing contemporary events, the outlook is bleak.

Failure to learn from Experience

One might expect rational people to respond in a logical manner to observed phenomena, to historical precedent and advice from specialised non-political experts, but regretfully there is no evidence to support these expectations. Perhaps it is the cumbersome nature of government itself that inhibits logical national decisions that most simple people would regard as common sense. The French fought in Indo-China for ten years with the best troops, material resources and weaponry that they could produce, but in the end they retreated, having decided that it was not possible to win. This recent historical example did not deter the most powerful nation in the world, the United States of America, from taking on the Vietnamese in a campaign that ended in slaughter, defeat and shame.

In the last century (1839-42) in Afghanistan, the British succeeded in conquering most of the nation in the first Afghan war. This was not accepted by the Afghans, who, after signing a peace treaty with the British, immediately massacred all but one of the British army of 3,000 men, the single survivor being allowed to return to India to bring the bad news of the disaster. A further attempt by the British to subjugate Afghanistan also met with failure. These two portrayals of what happens to invading armies in Afghanistan was apparently no deterrent to the Russians, who suffered a similar humiliation. Now, at the time of writing, the nation that was Yugoslavia has divided into warring factions perpetrating unspeakable atrocities on fellow citizens with whom they had lived in peace for many years. Hatreds going back over centuries have suppressed compassion between communities, whose main differences have been based on religious affiliation to the orthodox or catholic Christian churches and the Muslim religion.

Yugoslavia was created from part of the old Austro-Hungarian Empire and was politically stable as a communist state under Tito, but the old hatreds were simmering, just waiting to be released as soon as forceful restraints were removed. Western nations and the Muslim world look at this area of the Balkans in horror. Much rhetoric has been expressed as to how external force could be used to halt this carnage. The lessons of history would suggest that the price would be dear and a successful solution unlikely. The situation in the Balkans, and in Northern Ireland, of long-standing hatred, finally erupting into lethal violence, is not a necessary consequence for people of different religious or ethnic origins who inhabit the same area. There is multi-racial peaceful coexistence in Singapore, and Switzerland is another example of a nation where people, speaking different tongues and espousing different branches of the Christian Church, have lived in peace for a long time.

The ecological balance between living creatures, the atmosphere and the oceans has been overturned by mankind whose 'progress' has been made at the expense of other creatures and plants. The ever-increasing numbers of human beings with their destructive and aggressive tendencies are like a cancer of the earth that will spread and devour all living matter unless radical action is taken.

Is it conceivable that political regimes might work together to prevent a mega-war, stop the rape of the earth and control population without the need for war, famine and pestilence? The developed world has a prosperity which is based on trade and a productive industry. Economic growth is all-important for that prosperity and depends on consumer goods being wanted and purchased. There must be money available for this and a capacity to turn raw materials into products. This has worked well in the past in terms of making the rich countries richer. Coal, oil and gas have been consumed and not replaced. Poor countries have become even poorer as their populations have increased and in Africa the pestilence of AIDS has added to the misery of poverty and of local wars, drought and crop failure, all of which have caused the most dreadful famines in Somalia.

The Power of Economic Superiority

The conquest of other nations is no longer a popular pastime among the most powerful rich countries, but a new form of control is exerted through economic superiority. The remarkable success of the Japanese economy since the war, emulated by Taiwan and South Korea, has become a role model for developing countries, notably Malaysia, Thailand, Indonesia and China.

Nationalism based on ethnic and religious criteria usually leads to conflict and misery. In central Europe, and parts of the old Soviet Union and the Indian sub-continent, the strength of religious conviction, fanaticism and fundamentalism have become intensified: these are aggravated when there is poverty, especially where the poor are in obvious juxtaposition to the rich. In all democratic countries political power depends on popularity and popularity is achieved by short-term measures since elections are held every few years and politicians seldom look beyond them.

Although many western countries try to plan their economic development, in practice economists seem to be woefully wrong in their predictive ability. The discipline has multiple theories which seem to be repeatedly proven wrong by the unpredictable response of human beings to economic challenges. The rich western countries have enough food, although the distribution is uneven. Western Europe has a glut of many commodities due to efficient farming and artificial pricing of farm products. Most citizens have shelter, and communications are good. Television reigns supreme by penetrating almost every dwelling place. The power of television is enormous as was predicted by Orwell in his book *1984*. But 1984 has been and gone without any dramatic change occurring in that particular year. With satellite communications it is possible and probable that major events throughout the world, such as the massacre of the students in Tiananmen Square in 1989, will become available in every home, with all the horror and carnage clearly shown, and political commentary appropriate to the government where the television is being shown putting the events into perspective.

The need to stimulate the economy requires a large propaganda machine to persuade people that they need a new car, a new washing machine and other household appliances every two to three years. Programmed obsolescence is the hallmark of industry rather than the production of quality goods that will last for many years. In 'high-tech' apparatus such as computers, television sets, videos and electronic gadgetry, it is not necessary for obsolescence to be built in. Advances in the technology are so rapid that even perfectly working apparatus becomes obsolete and is rapidly superseded by a better product or at least a model with more facilities.

One of the most extraordinary changes in our behaviour over the last fifty years has been the ease with which it is possible to travel to any part of the world. Non-stop flights are available between London and Tokyo and thus in a twelve-hour period it is possible to go nearly half way round the world, while the costs of travel in the mega-jets have been reduced so that it is no longer a perquisite of the rich. Travel is available to the middle classes of the developed world, and not only available, but becoming more and more normally regarded as a necessary part of life. As tourism enables people from different racial and political backgrounds to mingle, this should be beneficial, but the travel itself harms the environment, utilising fossil fuels, and releasing noxious chemicals.

Variations in the market economies of the developed countries associated for the most part with democratic regimes have in the past few decades been a formula for success. Whether this is able to continue is not clear, but China with a totalitarian regime seems poised to take the same route. An authoritarian regime in a huge country is likely to have an inefficient and enormous bureaucracy with minor rules governing every activity. This is a sitting target for clever and corrupt people to circumvent and to manipulate to their own advantage. Those in power know that they themselves and the system they represent would be unlikely to survive a democratic revolution and for these reasons they cling desperately to the status quo. Mutual fear is perhaps the best protection from the dangers of a mega-war, but fear is irrelevant if fundamentalism is suitably fuelled by a fanatical belief in its righteousness, and especially if death will be rewarded by heaven in the promised next life.

Although there have been ecological conferences and many books have been written about the rape of the earth, and practical measures suggested to prevent the mass destruction of irreplaceable resources, pollution of the atmosphere and seas continues nevertheless and good intentions are usually overcome by national greed, the unprincipled exploitation of cheap labour by multinational companies and by criminal behaviour. Individual nations may feel that it benefits themselves to continue to over-fish the seas even if rare species are destroyed so that eventually the sea will no longer be able to provide any food. Ecological considerations usually fail to figure at all in the plans of greedy industrialists, using the mechanical chain saw to destroy, in a few days, large areas of rain forests with trees hundreds of years old, and the animal and vegetable life that depends on these beautiful mantles of our planet. All the worries outlined above will get worse unless the increase in population is controlled. The developed world seems to be in a relatively stable state of population and this appears to fit best into the economic and occupational aspirations of contemporary men and women. The population of the undeveloped world, however, is increasing deliberately and accidentally: deliberately on the part of individuals, even when governments recognise what is happening and try to persuade their citizens to practise birth control or coerce them in that direction, as in China.

Singapore

Not all governments are without hope. A political regime can work: for example, Singapore has a multi-racial flourishing society and it would appear to the outside visitor to be happy. I spent a year in Singapore in the 1950s. At that time the British Empire was waning, but the institutions of the empire, notably its schools, law enforcement and courts of justice, had been in existence for many years. Nevertheless, the citizens of different ethnic and religious origin were continually involved in conflict, often in bloody engagements in the streets. Chinese, Malay, Indian and European all seemed to hate each other, corruption was rife and the military power of Britain was only just able to keep the status quo. When Britain left, the brilliant Cambridge-educated lawyer, Lee Kuan Yew, the leader of the Peoples' Action Party, considered then by the British to be neo-communist, took power and shifted his philosophical doctrine increasingly to the right-wing of politics. In the course of thirty years Lee Kuan Yew's vision of Utopia in the city state of Singapore seems to have come to fruition. The different racial groups now live in harmony, the streets are safe and clean, the government as a secular 'big brother' advises its citizens how to behave so as not to offend individual religious sensibilities. Open dissent is not tolerated. The Peoples' Action Party always regarded it as a tragedy when one or two opposition candidates were elected who had wished to challenge the success story. Economic growth continues, there is health care for all, enough food, a disciplined education and rewards to those who are considered deserving.

There are also strict punishments for those who contravene the law. The visitor to Singapore will find on his arrival card the statement 'Welcome to Singapore', and on the reverse in red letters 'WARNING, death for drug traffickers under Singaporean law'. Though there is no real drug problem in Singapore, every year a few people carrying drugs, usually the pawns in the drug barons' chess game, are executed. There are severe fines for littering the streets, smoking in the wrong place, eating on the underground railway, and the sale of chewing gum is prohibited. Many misdemeanours are punished by flogging, as well as imprisonment, but the average Singaporean is happy with the way the country works. Taxi drivers and shopkeepers explain to the visitor how much better Singapore is than any other country, particularly the decadent West with its urban underclass, violence and drugs. You know they have a point.

In *The Economist*[20] Lee Kuan Yew, referring to progress in Asia, is quoted as follows:

> If we follow the West in our social relations and family structures, we will be in deep trouble. In the West the Christian religion used to instil fear of punishment in hell or reward in heaven. Science and technology have eliminated that fear. So the controlling mechanism has gone away. I am hoping that because Asian moral control is based on what is good in a secular this-world and not a spiritual after-world, we will not lose our moral bearings. That's the first point.
>
> The second point is we should not substitute the state for the parents or the family. If you bring a child into the world in the West, the state caters for him. That's dangerous. If you bring a child into Asia, that's your personal responsibility.
>
> As long as our society remains structured in this traditional way, we will be different. We will not allow muggers to clonk you on the head and grab your belongings and leave you dying or dead on the streets. And when you are ill you will not be abandoned because your family are required by culture to look after you or suffer shame.
>
> Good luck.

In trying to explain how Lee Kuan Yew's dreams have been realised, the answers are not certain, but the brilliance of Lee Kuan Yew himself, and the lack of corruption in the regime, would seem to be most important. If those in charge do not appear to the 'man in the street' to be corrupt, then strict rules for the good of the community are acceptable. Another factor important in Singapore's success is its geography. It is a city state surrounded by water, which facilitates control by the authorities, who are able to monitor foreign entries and avoid any movement of criminals and political agitators in and out of the country, thereby stopping the drug trade and other smuggling. There is a feeling of pride and success that can be directed in a patriotic way. The Singapore phenomenon is extraordinary and although many visitors have criticised the lack of a soul in Singapore and the poverty of its cultural pursuits, most citizens nevertheless appear to be happy, they are all well fed, and there is no obvious major political dissent in spite of a close mix in terms of living together of Chinese, Malays, Indians and a few Europeans.

---

[20] Copyright © *The Economist,* October 1993.

Rights of the Individual versus General Good

Is protection of the rights of the individual in liberal democratic societies interfering with the general good of the community? This is an interesting question that will have to be faced by all democracies. In every society lines are drawn concerning human behaviour and the infringement of certain rules that if tolerated will lead to a disintegration of civilisation and society. Theft, rape and murder are not acceptable. 'Live and let live' is the basis for enlightened, fruitful and harmonious co-existence, but free speech, and the freedom to walk in the streets in safety, are also an essential requirement of a civilised society.

In an autocratic repressive police-dominated regime the streets may be safe, but the minds of thoughtful creative people are in bondage: at the same time the loosening of all restrictions leads rapidly to anarchy. In the United States of America most large cities have extensive areas that are exceedingly dangerous to visit. In these 'war zones' any stranger is fair game for theft and murder, and rape is often an added hazard. Prominent police activity merely contains the violence, more young males languish in jails in the US than in any other country, more than one million, and nearly 50% of these are black although the population of black US citizens is 12%. It would seem that racial prejudice has in the past led to a ghetto criminal mentality in many young blacks, who, deprived of a happy childhood, get caught up in the drug culture of violence and extortion, with traditional family life being unusual.

At the other extreme most professionals and those involved in business and finance have luxurious life-styles. Doctors, especially those practising surgery, have large incomes, but in common with most successful people in the West they work very hard for long hours. Lawyers in the USA have increased in numbers in recent years and flourish exceedingly well. In order to get work they are prepared to take on cases that in most countries would be regarded as ludicrous and an affront to common sense and decency. The less successful will work on contingency to get their practices started.

If you stray into a war zone in a large American city you are liable to be robbed and may easily be killed. If you trip over the carpet in a friend's house after imbibing too many cocktails, a mark of your friend's hospitality, you will have no difficulty in finding a lawyer who will take on your case of injury by suing your friend for having dangerous carpets and giving you alcoholic drinks! If that may seem to be a hopeless case, you are wrong, since the lawyer would not accept the brief if there was not a good chance of winning and the lawyer will receive 50% of the damages as contingency fees. Your feckless behaviour and betrayal of your friend's hospitality benefits the lawyers, but insurance companies suffer if your friend is insured; if not he may be impoverished. No wonder many American citizens, observing the preponderance of lawyers in politics and in society in general, believe that their country is run by lawyers for the benefit of lawyers. In the USA there is one lawyer for every 350 citizens, in Japan the ratio is 25 times lower, 1 to 8,800, which may help explain why Japan in recent years has been so successful.

How far can the controls of individual freedom be relaxed before other citizens suffer? Amplified music played continuously in one unit of an apartment block can drive the neighbours to violence or suicide unless they are protected by law against the nuisance. Lack of discipline in schools can prevent all classroom education. A small number of disruptive aggressive children can terrorise a teacher and fellow pupils, so that trying to maintain order may be a full time occupation for the teacher, subjected to siege tactics, not allowed to chastise violent children or impose any kind of punishment that will deter bullying. There is no easy solution in a liberal society to control anti-social children who have no wish to learn anything and are happy to prevent the majority from studying and becoming educated. This is a very serious matter in some British schools. Any whisper of touching a child who is unruly will produce an instantaneous and intimidating investigation by the social services, some of whose officers are like 'the secret police' of the liberal society. They often respond uncritically to anonymous information and can bring misery to blameless individuals and break up families.

Gun Laws

In America the lax gun laws are seen by outsiders as a direct and important cause of the serious escalation of urban violence. Guns are freely available in many states and millions of citizens own hand and automatic guns which they use, often with little provocation, in domestic situations that would incur only minor violence if the gun were not readily to hand. Criminals know that violent crime will be much easier and more successful if guns are used than without lethal weapons. Public reaction to the murder statistics was reflected in the reintroduction and the carrying out of the death penalty in many states, which is seen not merely as a punishment for the criminals but as a deterrent to others; in Voltaire's words (when Admiral Byng was executed by a Royal Naval firing squad for incompetence) 'Pour encourager les autres'. In Seattle assaults involving firearms are seven times higher than in Vancouver, fifty miles away in Canada, where there are severe restrictions and penalties for the possession of guns.

It would seem that liberal democratic societies can and do allow individual freedoms to interfere with the welfare of the majority of law-abiding citizens. An uncontrolled, potentially violent, underclass is the result, at least in part, of poor, undisciplined education, insufficient and inadequate housing, lack of traditional family life, a weakening in the power and influence of religion, the ready availability of guns and drugs, unemployment, and the birth of children to immature, impoverished, feckless parents.

Automation, a product of applied science, is likely to increase unemployment and poverty. Nevertheless in rich countries the rich get richer, and there are many lucrative professions that contribute little to the welfare of society, especially those of lawyers and bureaucrats. But the work ethic is powerful, and often nearly pathological in those who are self-employed in occupations that reward effort with money. Meanwhile many employed by the state and other large impersonal institutions long to retire or to be released from the requirement to work by medical certificates for imagined illness. When a patient recovering from injury or operation asks 'Can I go back to work now?', he or she usually works for himself or herself, or is one of the very lucky few who really enjoy their work.

Employment

Developments in manufacturing in the West are leading to increasing automation and some products are now made with a minimal requirement of human labour. This robotic manufacturing is bound to increase since it is more efficient and is not subject to the vagaries of employed labour. The 'robot minder' will require skilled training in the control of the computer programmes. The production of food will also become increasingly mechanical with bio-technology using genetically transformed edible plants, fungi and animals, so the output of both food and manufactured goods will increase, but job opportunities will diminish and already unemployment is a major worry in most developed countries.

The only industries that will still require large labour forces are the health and welfare services, the police, armed forces and prisons. Once again, applied science is disturbing the innate biological programme of man and animals. In the past the evolution of man has not resulted from the survival of the most idle and the least fit, but this is what is now happening. The health and welfare services will continue to expand as more people with previously lethal conditions are prevented from dying and the ageing population increases. Men and women over the age of seventy-five, mentally and physically fit, are lucky because they can enjoy an independent existence, but ill health in the aged is a terrible burden for the afflicted individuals and those caring for them. For patients born with severe brain damage or serious physical handicap, the situation is similar. The quality of life will be poor, and it is as if they had reached the degenerative state of old age without going through a period of normal existence. The care needed for the crippled and the mentally infirm is very demanding and expensive, and it requires the labour-intensive effort of dedicated carers. The quality of life of the increasingly large numbers of unemployed is also poor. Welfare handouts will seldom be adequate to avoid a strong temptation to get involved in the 'black' economy or in criminal activity. There is no doubt that an individual of working age who is gainfully employed in an occupation that he or she finds enjoyable and demanding is very fortunate.

Youth is endowed with great reserves of energy, and the cravings for excitement and danger are common features of young males. In the past in western countries there were numerous possibilities for adventure in the legitimate professions of soldiering and administration in the colonies. If things at home were not to the liking of ambitious young men, they could emigrate to distant lands. All these opportunities have now gone and it is extremely difficult to see a solution to the aspirations of dissatisfied, poorly educated youths with aggressive tendencies. Modern living in civilised countries seems to involve an increasing amount of time spent watching a rectangular screen: the word processor or a computer when at work, and the television for relaxation. The most popular television programmes have a large content of violence, often particularly brutal and gratuitous. This can be supplemented by even more dreadful, depraving drama, portrayed in cheap video cassettes. The average American child has witnessed 40,000 murders on television by the age of eighteen.[21] This 'educational' facility provides malcontents with powerful instruction on how to channel their violent tendencies to cause maximum unhappiness to others.

These observations are bad enough with the present population distribution, which, as we have seen, has been carefully arranged to divide roughly into equal numbers of males and females, but once again, the application of science is about to have a major influence for change. It is already possible to determine the sex of a baby well before birth, so that a deliberate abortion can get rid of a foetus of the unwanted sex and it is likely that we will soon be able to have a reliable method of sex selection by means of choosing the sperm with the chromosome of the sex that is desired. It would seem unlikely that the wishes of potential parents would fit exactly into half male and half female. In developing countries most parents prefer male to female children, which could result in a great excess of young males. A relative decrease in the proportion of females would lead to a fall in the total number of births and might help to contain the population explosion. This seems to be happening in China. Although females are fully capable of anti-social and violent behaviour, these characteristics are far more natural and common in males, so the more young males, the more the risk of trouble. A large police and para-military force will be needed to try to maintain law and order, but it is unlikely that even a major increase in officers of the law would be able to contain serious violence if there was an incident that raised the passions of most of the underclass, as occurred in Los Angeles in the early nineties.

The above considerations relating to unemployment have dwelt on prospects for the developed nations but there is also a worrying outlook for poor countries. The flow of cheap manufactured goods and bio-technologically produced food from the West will further weaken the farming communities, and the drift from rural areas to the cities in the developing countries will continue at an ever increasing rate which, together with the huge population increase, will swell the ranks of ghetto shanty towns that are already a shameful obscenity in some mega-cities of the world, such as Bombay, Calcutta, Rio de Janeiro and Mexico City. There will be a powerful urge to emigrate from these dreadful social poverty traps to more prosperous areas and countries and this will be accompanied by a serious danger of armed conflict. Since the population of the developing countries will be superior numerically, North America and the West might need to defend their frontiers with high-tech weapons which would probably not, *in extremis*, exclude nuclear devices. It is only by a drastic curtailment of the population increase in developing

---

[21] JAMA 1993 vol. 270, no. 23 p 2870

countries and careful thought given to new developments in manufacturing and the bio-production of food that we may be able to avert dangerous conflict.

Recreational Activities

To find an occupation for the frustrated young unemployed that will not endanger the security of the State and the peaceful coexistence of the citizens has been a worry for politicians since the time of Nero who provided circuses for the masses. The circuses were violent spectacles with gladiators fighting to the death and people recognised as 'enemies of society' being thrown to the lions. The situation has changed little except that instead of such live spectacles of death and suffering, we are now supplied with similar spectacles in our households every evening on the television screen. To cope with the frustrated, pent-up energy of young males who do not have suitable occupations, there will need to be much more effort devoted to providing harmless gladiatorial combat, for example on the football field or in athletics encounters. If sufficient interest and enthusiasm can be generated by participating and supporting team sports this may divert youngsters from stealing cars and killing themselves and innocent bystanders, and in indulging in other criminal activities. Sporting encounters allow the expression of competitive instincts which do not generally result in harm. Looking back towards our evolution and animal behaviour, presumably our love of sport is directly related to the co-operative hunting skill and combat with rivals that can be observed in many animal species, including our nearest relatives, the chimpanzees. It will be important to provide sufficient outlets for the youth who need not or cannot work, to divert them from finding excitement in nihilistic pursuits, such as the drug culture and crime.

Education

The pattern of education varies in different parts of the world. In England children aiming for university tend to specialise in a few topics early when still at school, and then remain confined to their chief options, usually of one or two subjects. In the United States of America school and university education is broader and this probably results in the potential for a more 'rounded' person at the end of a bachelor's degree, but in the best graduate schools the competition is so fierce that few students are able to maintain much interest in subjects outside of the direct vocational requirements. Probably all higher education, world-wide, would benefit from the required teaching of general science for arts students and vice versa.

Ageing

In many animal species, including primates closely related to man, survival into old age is unusual because of disease, weakness and especially the loss of ability to hunt, forage and to eat food. Thus loss of teeth, poor eyesight, sense of smell and hearing which deteriorate with age, impair the ability to survive in a community not programmed to help the incapable. In man the situation is different, and humans can survive with extreme infirmity if they are assiduously cared for, fed, cleaned and looked after with compassion. The time of the onset of infirmity in old age, and the inability to live an independent existence, can be postponed by modern medical treatment, particularly the preserving of eyesight by corrective glasses, surgical treatment of cataracts and conservative management of tooth decay and false dentures. The locomotor system can be propped up by joint replacement often enabling somebody completely crippled with continuous pain to be able to return to vigorous activity. We can treat infections, cure weaknesses of the muscles that are causing hernias, remove obstructing portions of bowel and restore the blocked drainage of vital organs such as the kidneys, the liver and the pancreas. The horizons of therapeutic medicine have been widened to an enormous extent in recent years. Living vital organs can be replaced and as results of this type of treatment improve, so the organ to be transplanted assumes an ever increasing value to the recipient, far in excess of money and jewels. A consideration of the debased behaviour that some human beings will engage in to acquire wealth would suggest that there is a danger that similar corrupt and criminal activities may be devoted to obtaining organs when they are in short supply. This is just another example of a small but potential danger that could lead to unethical medical practice. There are increasing numbers of aged people in the developed countries, while in the poorer nations, as medical care improves, so will the population also age. One occupation for the jobless young could be to take care of the elderly in society, as well as younger individuals handicapped by physical or mental disability.

Euthanasia

In a civilised country if a pet dog or cat is suffering pain from an incurable disease or has become so old as to be unable to walk or eat, the accepted ethical practice is to administer a painless lethal dose of a barbiturate. To keep ill or decrepitly aged pets alive by artificial means would be considered cruel. Animal protection societies in western countries would order euthanasia for the afflicted pet and seek punishment of the owners.

How is it that we do not have a similar compassionate feeling towards afflicted members of our own species? Probably compassion is widespread but there are fears of abuse, particularly where inherited wealth is concerned, and the longer life continues the smaller the inheritance. Although people in good health might readily opt for euthanasia in the event that they developed a painful, incurable illness, feelings change with circumstances and time. Could all members of the family be trusted with honest testimony as to how incapacitated their sick relative was and how much pain they appeared to be suffering? How would doctors feel, charged with administering a lethal drug? The greater the bureaucracy associated with euthanasia, the less the likelihood of abuse, but then also the process of going through the safeguards could be extremely distasteful for a caring family.

In Holland euthanasia is legal under strictly defined circumstances, but other western countries have not followed suit. In the past it was often left to the compassionate integrity of the medical profession to care for the desperately afflicted. The doctor would give dangerous doses of painkilling or sedative drugs, or withhold powerful antibiotics or avoid surgery, when it was felt that this was the kindest course for the sick patient. This applies not only to the elderly but also to younger people with incurable painful diseases and children born with terrible birth defects. Usually the doctor would confer with the closest relatives explaining the options and make a joint decision with them. Recently there has been a demand for more openness in medical decision-making which has a tendency to infringe the personal confidence between doctor, patient and family, bringing third parties into the process, and I suspect that this has not in general been beneficial.

The arguments for euthanasia, just as the arguments for therapeutic eugenics, are seductive, but medical opinions framed in legal documents and made available to government officials are likely to frighten off the medical profession. The increasing tendency to sue doctors for negligence can result in harmful defensive medicine which is often not in the patient's best interest, so similar attitudes would tend to develop if euthanasia was legalised.

There would seem to be much in favour of strengthening ethical teaching in the medical profession and leaving the decisions relating to treatment or non-treatment of patients to the patient, the doctor and the family. Any abuse in 'getting rid of' old or useless, physically and mentally incapacitated people would denigrate society to the level practised by the Nazis. To remain civilised we must take care of those handicapped or in pain, but treatment should not be directed solely to the preservation of life if this is against the wishes of the patient and the family.

It has been accepted as proper for the medical profession since the time of Hipocrates for a doctor to give increasing doses of painkilling or sedative drugs to alleviate the suffering of a patient. To kill deliberately a patient who is suffering is not part of medicine, it is an execution; the only purpose of the act is to kill. A knife or a gun could be used instead of a syringe. Euthanasia means an easy death, but the doctor's role should not be that of a killer. 'Thou shalt not kill but needst not strive officiously to keep alive.'[22]

'Utopia'?

Is the Singapore success story a good model on which to base political structures elsewhere? In democratic, developed countries Lee Kuan Yew would not be acceptable because of the authoritarian strict government control of drug trafficking, the punishments of crime and intolerant attitude to critics. In most democratic countries the Darwinian pressure on evolution or the survival of the fittest in a hostile environment has changed so that now, thanks to modern medicine and the social use of government funds, those unfit in society can survive and are treated compassionately. Patients with debilitating diseases that were previously lethal can

---

[22] Arthur Hugh Clough, English poet 1819-1861, *The Latest Decalogue*

be cared for and it is likely that inherited disorders, which used to be fatal, will become increasingly common as new strategies of treatment are developed. Before insulin was available the common form of juvenile diabetes was an extremely distressing illness with inexorable emaciation and death in childhood. The disease tends to occur in families with an inherited marker and since most diabetics now survive well beyond childbearing age, this marker of susceptibility to diabetes and the disease itself will become increasingly common. Scientific medicine is responsible for the low rate of deaths in childhood, and of deaths in women associated with childbirth, and also in the successful treatment of many previously lethal conditions.

In this chapter I have examined certain political systems. It would seem that most current political regimes, even if they are sufficiently aware of the dangers of overpopulation, do not have the will or the structure to exert the necessary control. This leaves only one satisfactory solution, namely the co-operation of all nations on this all-important issue. Some suggestions as to how this might come about will be discussed later, but the conflict of the virtues of discipline, as in a strong political regime or fundamentalist religious state, and the lack of individual freedom that must necessarily follow are hard to reconcile.

Chapter 9

Biology of Human Reproduction

'Go forth and multiply' was God's instruction to the children of Israel, but the urge to multiply had already been programmed into all living matter. The arrangement of the DNA in the chromosomes is to split the genetic material into two and then remake the missing half in the new cell. This is an essential component of the cell division necessary for the development of an egg into an individual and for most of the tissues of the body to maintain themselves in a healthy state. It has been known since the early part of this century that prior to division, the chromosomes, which we now know to be composed of genes built of DNA in its double helical structure, split into two chromatids which become arranged on a spindle rather like a complicated washing line and then one chromatid goes to each of the daughter cells resulting from the division. The new nucleus is re-assembled by each chromatid becoming a full chromosome rather like an imprint from a seal (see Appendix I).

The differentiation of cells into the separate organs and tissues of the body is only beginning to be understood. Certain growth factors are liberated in different parts of the early embryo to instruct or select cells to develop into, for instance, blood vessels, kidneys, brain, liver, heart. In man once the embryo is fully developed and the child is born, most cells in the body continue to grow by division or by the cells themselves individually enlarging. The first is called hyperplasia and the second hypertrophy. The neurones of the brain and the beta cells of the pancreas that produce insulin are examples of cells that cannot divide and we are stuck with the number that are present at birth. The only thing that can happen, and does happen, is that with time there is attrition and some of the cells die and cannot be replaced. This explains the loss of mental ability with age and the frequent occurrence of diabetes of mature onset, a disease that is different from the juvenile diabetes already mentioned.

The cell division so far considered, mitosis, is similar in kind to the asexual division of an amoeba, but in the case of the amoeba, the division results in two free-living individuals consisting each of only one cell (*figure* 11). Most animals and plants have another form of division which permits the mixing of DNA and variations in genetic material, and therefore physical and biochemical characteristics. This form of reproduction is called sexual reproduction, and the process is more complicated than simple cell division (see Appendix I).

Sexual Reproduction

For sexual reproduction to occur specialised organs are necessary in which the germ cells are produced each with half the number of chromosomes present in the rest of the cells in the body, and this division is called meiosis. One pair of chromosomes, the sex chromosomes, is asymmetric in the male, the arrangement

Cell Division : Mitosis

Chromosomes consist each of a long DNA molecule plus protein. There are 46 chromosomes in man. The DNA first replicates itself in the nucleus forming 2 mirror image **chromatids** for each chromosome.

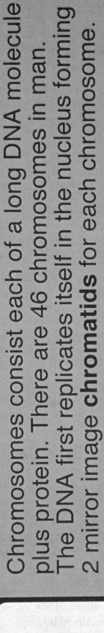

A spindle forms of fine fibres. Each replicated 2 chromatid chromosome attaches itself to a fibre at the equator of the spindle

The chromatids separate and move to the poles of the spindle

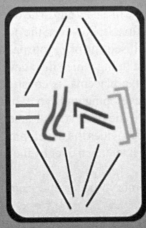

Figure 11. Mitosis

being XY, in the female it is XX. When sperms are formed with half or haploid chromosome content, 50% are X and 50% are Y but all unfertilised eggs are X. Thus the sex chromosome of the sperm determines the sex of the offspring. The mature male germ cell or spermatozoon is motile with an extremely active propellant tail and a head that consists of little more than the haploid DNA package. The female germ cell contains a similar DNA haploid package, but in addition material that can nourish the fusion or fertilisation of the male and female DNA to provide an environment suitable for the early divisions of the embryo cells (*figures* 12 & 13).

The female germ cells, the oocytes, are the largest cells in the body, huge in relation to the male sperms, and they develop in the ovaries of females; the maturation process continues until puberty. The number of egg cells has reached the maximum at birth and no new ones can be produced, although there will probably be half a million in each ovary, but the number that will actually be capable of fertilisation is very much less. There are enough to provide fertile periods in each month until the menopause at around the age of fifty. In contrast, the many billions of male germ cells are continually produced until old age, although the number of sperms and their ability to fertilise become impaired in old age as does the ability to complete a successful coital act.

The sex hormones that circulate in the blood are produced in the main by the testis in the male and the ovaries in the female, in both cases under the control of chemical hormones produced in the pituitary gland just beneath the brain. The sex hormones are responsible for the secondary sexual characteristics. A beard grows on the face in the male, and at the same time the shape of the larynx changes so that the voice deepens, and there is also growth of pubic hair, and an enlargement of the penis and testes. These changes are accompanied by the physical growth of the long bones. In the female, the secondary characteristics are the developments of active breast tissue with an enlargement of the breasts, the growth of pubic hair and then the liberation of eggs from the ovaries each month into the fallopian tubes where fertilisation becomes possible.

The lining of the uterus is prepared for the reception of the embryo with a chemical signal released from the ovary into the bloodstream, which causes the surface lining to become increasingly vascularised and receptive for implantation of the egg. If fertilisation does not occur the egg dies and the ovaries go through the process of preparing for the release of a new egg. The over-ripe lining of the uterus dies and is shed as the menstrual flux. If, however, the ovum is fertilised by a sperm in the fallopian tube, then the fertilised egg or zygote passes down to the uterus and becomes embedded in the uterine lining which then develops more blood vessels; a specialised nutritional organ, the placenta, is constructed, consisting of blood vessels going to and from the developing embryo, while maternal blood vessels carry nourishment and oxygen to the embryo and take away wastes and carbon dioxide. The placenta, therefore, provides the developing embryo with respiratory and alimentary functions that are later taken over by the lungs, the stomach and the intestines.

As the cell divisions in the embryo occur and primitive organs develop, the

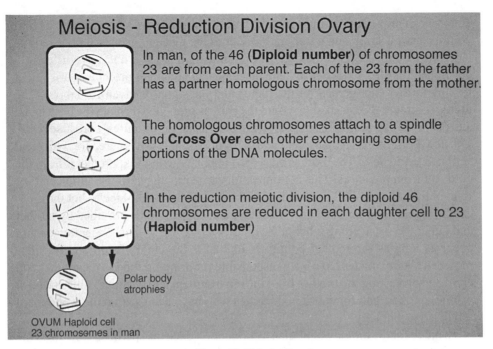

Figure 12. Meiosis - Female

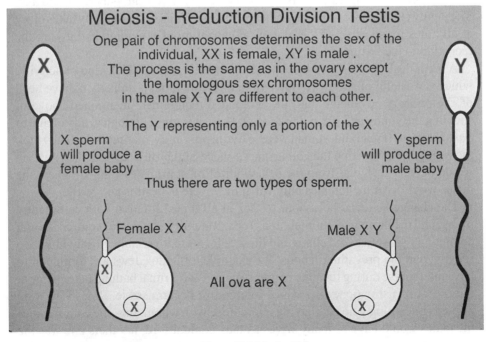

Figure 13. Meiosis - Male

embryo can move around in its own private swimming pool, the amniotic cavity, with its heart beating and pumping blood into the placenta from which it returns laden with nourishment and oxygen. After nine months the embryo is sufficiently developed for birth to take place, the placenta can no longer provide nourishment for any further enlargement of the foetus and the signal is given for labour. The uterus contracts, the cervix dilates and the baby is propelled through the birth canal and out of the vagina where it takes its first breath and the umbilical cord is severed. The new-born child is helpless and will certainly die unless it is cared for with great skill and tenderness. The mother must feed the baby with milk, protect it from the cold and from predators. This continues for some months until the child can take food independent of milk, coinciding with the development of teeth, but the child cannot gather food for itself and will require each meal to be provided by mother and father. Breast-feeding inhibits the mother's ovaries, so that conception cannot occur as long as the mother continues to suckle the child. Traditionally, since recorded history, males have been responsible for bringing food to the mother and child and protecting the mother from the environment and enemies. This is true in primitive tribes, and for aboriginal natives who have been spared the wonders of 'civilised technology'.

So much for the biology of human reproduction once the sperm has fertilised the egg, but getting the sperm to a position where it can fertilise the egg is an important activity that has exercised the minds and bodies of men and women since *homo sapiens* emerged from the ape-like *homo erectus*. Attraction between man and woman and the desire to copulate is different in humans compared to most other animal species; sexual intercourse can occur at any time from puberty to old age. The pigmy chimpanzee is the only other primate in which sexual activity takes place at all times irrespective of the biological capability of providing and giving the reception to the fertilised egg.

A great deal of effort will be expended in sterile mating. This kind of activity, which is wasteful of energy resources and therefore food, is unlikely to have been of evolutionary advantage until the prolonged requirement mentioned above of suckling the young and providing food and care became a biological advantage to *homo sapiens*. If man and woman were to live in proximity, mating as the fancy took them and then protecting the young once a successful birth occurred, the situation would be very different from the behaviour of most primates studied, where the males would visit the females only when they were in oestrus and fertile.

The change in social behaviour to 'sex at all times' fitted in with community living, and the farming of animals and crops. Rules of living were required in each community so as to avoid chaos and these rules were invariably closely linked to religion and the prevailing taboos: for example, orthodox Jews are forbidden to have intercourse during the time of menstruation and a ritual bathing takes place at the end of menstruation, after which intercourse is permissible. Rules also were needed concerning who was having intercourse with whom. In some communities the males would have as many wives as they could afford, in others one was the maximum. A few communities were polyandrous, the opposite to polygamy, the women being permitted more than one husband. In contemporary western society sequential polygamy and polyandry are not uncommon, interposed by divorce. With a few exceptions studied throughout the world and in recorded history, the rules have been very strict, transgression being severely punished, but on the other hand, fecundity and the birth of a healthy child are considered by all communities to be a blessing, often celebrated with a religious service and sometimes ceremonies that anticipated the event to bring about fecundity in cattle and crops as well as in humans. Fertility rites and then the thanksgiving of successful fertility, the harvest festival, have featured in many different societies.

The securing of a mate might be accompanied by certain rituals often involving elders in the family, even special selections made by priests. Money and tokens were often exchanged or sometimes required to purchase the bride or came as additional gifts with the bride as a dowry. The courtship, fertility rites and harvest festival often were accompanied by the playing of drums, dancing and music, all considered as culture and often requiring the recitation of poems and prayers.

Inherited courtship rituals can be readily observed in animals: the display of the peacock, the songs between birds and the cries between mating animals. One of the most beautiful courtships that I witnessed is the dance of the blue footed booby. The male approaches the female on the ground where they roost and proceeds to perform a complicated dance around the female who initially stands still without any betrayal of emotion. The male then gets worked up and produces a quite hectic and frenetic fandango and if the female persists in remaining still, the male departs exhausted and presumably disappointed, perhaps looking to start the whole thing again with another female. However, if the female is interested in the male, she will also start to dance and they will perform together, the male dancing much more quickly than the female (*figure* 14). This appears to cement the bond between the birds who will mate and stay together as partners, both tending the eggs and feeding the young. A rather gruesome example of a hostile environment, scarce resources and mortality is part of the normal behaviour of another booby, the masked species. Two eggs are usually hatched and two babies born but one is fed all the delicacies and therefore the other fails to thrive and is eventually eaten by the bigger, spoiled and well-fed chick. This seems to be an accepted part of existence for all except the chick that gets eaten. I mention the animal models because it is clear that the ritual of mate selection, copulation, fertilisation, the bearing of babies and their nourishment is common to many vertebrate species. Fish frequently indulge in sexual reproduction by an indirect method. The female lays her haploid eggs in the water and the male deposits sperm close to the eggs so the fertilisation occurs without any physical contact between the male and female fish. Selective fertilisation without copulation is used in artificial insemination in the production of livestock and in treating infertile couples who wish to have babies.

There is a great excess of primitive oocytes in humans which will allow the release of one potentially fertilisable egg or ovum each month ensuring that there are far more possibilities for production of progeny than will ever be realised. In the male the odds on a given sperm fertilising an egg are exceedingly remote:

Figure 14. 'Courting Dance of the Bluefoot Booby' by Roy Calne

billions of sperm are expended on behalf of the one presumably lucky individual that reaches the haploid ovum which it can penetrate and fertilise. This over-production of seed in relation to the expectation of free living progeny is common throughout the animal and plant kingdom.

In humans the onset of puberty in the female heralds the fertile period which is terminated by the menopause. This is the phase during which babies might be conceived, and having been conceived the chances of an individual live-born infant reaching maturity were until recently poor. Many children died at the time of childbirth, many mothers died from obstructed labour, bleeding, or infection after the birth of a baby and the children that did survive frequently succumbed to infectious diseases such as measles, whooping cough, diphtheria and tuberculosis. All these hazards have been virtually eliminated in the developed world and there have been improvements in health care in the undeveloped nations pursued with vigour by medical missionaries and other men and women of good will, so that throughout the world infant and maternal mortality rates are falling. But there has been little sign of diminution in fecundity and childbirth. Encouragement to limit the family has not worked well where it has been tried, and in many countries it has not been tried.

Orthodox Catholicism forbids birth control which has also been prohibited by certain political regimes, but in the past two decades the facts have begun to sink into the heads of politicians and religious leaders throughout the world that unlimited procreation, the 'going forth and multiplying' of the Bible, cannot be encouraged, since the resources for unlimited population growth do not exist. The General Synod of the Church of England at its 1993 meeting appealed to the Pope to abandon the opposition of the Catholic church to contraception, but so far without success.

In the context of modern medicine, if the ovum could no longer be fertilised after the mother had given birth to two children, then the population would cease to increase, and would in fact slowly fall, since not all women of childbearing age want or can have children. There are serious political and religious difficulties in the implementation of any kind of birth control, particularly since the mainstream of advice and exhortation comes from developed countries trying to change the behaviour of those who are poor and already short of food and shelter.

Contraception

There is an apocryphal story of a young lady sitting next to an eminent gynaecologist at dinner who asked *sotto voce* what was the best form of contraception and he replied, 'A glass of ice cold water.' 'Really,' she whispered, 'Should one take it before or afterwards?' 'Instead!' was the reply. This rather unhelpful advice would certainly not help to manage the population crisis, but a simple, aesthetically acceptable long-lasting reversible contraceptive would be welcomed by millions of women living in impoverished circumstances burdened by young children and the fear of another pregnancy. Many women would prefer a safe permanent sterilisation, especially if this did not require a surgical operation.

Breast-feeding prevents ovulation and this form of natural contraception only allowed conception every three or four years in many poor rural communities where children were breast-fed until they were toddlers. Now the reduction of the period of breast feeding, and the introduction of powdered milk feeds for babies, removes this breathing space between pregnancies. In developed countries the age of puberty in females is falling, so the chances of early pregnancy involving a mature body, but an immature mind, are increasing.

The deliberate wish to avoid conception has prompted many different approaches in the past including interrupting the sexual act at the crucial moment (*coitus interruptus*), and developing careful programmes of timing to avoid the moment of ovulation when fertilisation is likely to occur. Both these approaches are unreliable. More effective was the introduction of barrier mechanical methods, or chemical gels, designed to kill the sperm. Mechanical methods may be in the form of a rubber cap fitting over the cervix, or one of the new female sheath-type contraceptives, but by far the most effective barrier is the contraceptive sheath or condom. The use of high quality latex and checks for leaks during manufacture makes the condom a reliable birth control agent and also an excellent barrier to the spread of sexually transmitted diseases including AIDS. The condom must be used properly but many couples find the sheath unacceptable, interfering with the male's pleasure and the psychology of the sexual act.

Deliberate chemical interference with the menstrual cycle with the contraceptive pill to stop ovulation changed sexual behaviour, especially in North America and the Western nations from the sixties. The 'pill' modifies the hormonal environment of the body, stopping the signal for the release of the ovum from the ovary, but menstruation is not affected. The side effects of the pill were worrying, but new low dose oral contraceptives have few side effects and for many are preferable to barrier techniques, while injected contraceptives can last for three months.

Recently, 'depot' forms of hormonal contraceptives have been introduced. Norplant is effective for up to five years after six flexible capsules are introduced under the skin, by a procedure similar to an injection. Quinacrine administered as a pellet into the neck of the womb blocks the fallopian tubes permanently. One-shot long-acting contraceptives or sterilisation procedures are preferable in many poor communities, especially if they are provided free. Norplant is now available in the UK under the National Health Service. Quinacrine is being used in Vietnam and other Asian countries and offers non-complicated sterilisation to women seeking permanent infertility.

The traditional sterilisation methods are ligation and division of the ovarian tubes in the female and vasectomy in the male. Reversal is complicated and often unsuccessful. The new intra-uterine devices have few side effects but they may act by causing very early abortion. There is an important psychological and philosophical difference between a hormonal contraceptive that prevents release or fertilisation of an ovum, and one that results in expulsion of a fertilised zygote, the latter being unacceptable to many, because the ovum has been fertilised. Potts[23] has pointed out that effective contraception reduces the demand for surgical abortion which is still high in many countries. One and a half million abortions are performed annually in the USA.

Progress has been made with a vaccination approach to contraception which is applicable to males and females, where the principle is to induce, with the vaccine, antibodies that inhibit the ability of the sperm to fertilise the egg. This is the most promising approach for the future. The possibility of linking a contraceptive to a harmless virus has already been explored with some success using the innocuous vaccinia virus as a vector. A protein from the capsule of the ovum, ZP3, when linked to the virus, causes the body to produce antibodies against ZP3 which stops the sperm from fertilising the ovum. If such an acceptable form of birth control were available, it would be a major task to persuade people to use it because of the worry that viruses might cause unexpected harm. The very word 'virus' invokes fear and prejudice. This obstacle may not be insurmountable. There is evidence of a strong wish amongst many of the poorer communities in the world, both in developed and in underdeveloped nations, to limit their families, so that the mother can have a reasonable quality of life without always being burdened by an infant to take care of both emotionally and financially. Birth control which is not a financial penalty, and without perceptible risk, would probably be far more acceptable than has been believed in the past. Many poor Indonesians have accepted birth control with a consequent reduction in the rate of population increase which resulted in an award to the Indonesian Government by the World Health Organisation.

To be readily acceptable, any long-term form of contraception would need to be potentially reversible. After the birth of two healthy children many women would welcome a simple painless method of permanent sterilisation. Both these options are now available. The next and much greater task will be to provide a comprehensive contraceptive service using the new techniques backed with encouragement from governments which should grant tax advantages to families limited to two children.

---

[23] Malcolm Potts, Professor of Population Studies, University of California, Berkeley, USA.

Chapter 10

Sex-Drive, Family Aspirations and National Ambitions

One fact is absolutely certain, all animals and plants that come into the world alive will die. The inevitability of mortality is of course a matter of singular concern to humans. Whether animals or plants can worry about the subject is not known. But, the span of life allotted, provided there is no catastrophe, varies in different species. A butterfly may die in a day and some trees will survive for hundreds of years, but during that life-time reproduction must occur, otherwise the species will become extinct. Reproduction by binary fission, the way in which cells divide, is possible in some species such as the amoeba and other unicellular organisms. Many plants can reproduce both sexually and asexually by cloning. Most species are reproduced by sexual means with a chance to mingle the DNA of two different individuals. The difference between sexual reproduction and cloning is important.

Cloning

A cloned individual is similar to unicellular organisms that are divided by binary fission. The DNA in each would be identical and remain so apart from chance mutations produced, for example, by x-rays or chemicals. Identical twins who developed from the same egg and have identical diploid chromosomal constitutions are a well-known example of cloned humans. A consideration of twins helps an understanding of what would happen if it were possible to clone humans from a diploid human cell: for instance, if the diploid nucleus from an adult human blood cell could be reverted to the same pre-differentiation state as a fertilised egg; such a procedure can be done, for example, in frogs, from embrional cells; then if the artificial egg was implanted, in humans, into a receptive uterus as a lodger, a successful pregnancy would produce a baby of identical chromosomal constitution as the individual from which it originally came. It would have the same inherited potential as the 'parent' had as a baby, but separated in time from the original stock, unlike identical twins that are born on the same day. Although the cloned individual would have the same inherited potential, he or she would have failed, of course, to inherit any of the ideas, impressions and memories that the 'single parent' had acquired in the course of education, illness, experience of life, joy and disappointment. All these acquired experiences are extremely important in the maturing of personality: as long as the brain is working well, experience will continue to educate. However, as neurones deteriorate with natural wear and tear, or due to poor nutrition from a bad blood supply, or a disease such as Alzheimer's, so the personality will fail to be able to recall from this rich store of experience and there will be cerebral deterioration. The cloned individual will have to go through his or her own acquired experience. This nurture will then be added to the nature, which being the same as the original stem individual will tend to respond to given external environmental happenings in a similar way, just as identical twins will tend to react in a similar

94

manner when separated at birth; they will often marry similar spouses and have occupations that have similarities, even developing the same diseases at about the same time. The cloned individual, although containing the same DNA arrangement in every cell as the parent stem, would nevertheless have his or her unique personality. A simple analogy would be that they are the same violin, but different tunes will be played on it according to environmental encounters.

This apparently tangential discourse arose from a consideration of the consequences of cloning, but I think it is important because, although mortality is certain, there seems a very fundamental urge in all living animals and plants to maintain the existence of their DNA. Although cloning would do this perfectly, it would not provide the cloned individual with the same personality as the parent from which it came.

An Understanding of our DNA and the Potential and Dangers of Genetic Engineering

We have seen that Harvey by observation and logical deduction postulated the existence of the capillary blood vessels in the circulation, although he could not see them. This concept was vital to an understanding of the circulation of the blood. Darwin painstakingly marshalled his evidence of evolution from his observation, but he lacked any data on the mechanism of genetics. Mendel produced a mathematical model of inheritance without any knowledge of the nature of the factors responsible.

It is now forty years since the double helix structure of DNA was discovered by Watson and Crick. We have developed a good understanding in chemical terms of how inheritance occurs, and an explanation of how sexual reproduction results in a mixing of inherited 'characters'. This variation sets the stage for the right environmental factors to enable us to select the fittest for survival in a biological evolutionary progress.

There is a major international scientific enterprise in progress to examine the structure of the whole of the human genome. Complimentary work is being undertaken in many laboratories throughout the world. What will we do with this knowledge?

Transgenic and Transfecting Technology

Genetic engineering has already developed into practical applications. Bacteria and yeast can be manipulated by the use of human genes in techniques called 'recombinant DNA synthesis' to produce specific proteins, for example human insulin to treat diabetes. Portions of DNA can be introduced into the fertilised egg and will then be part of the individual. The DNA may be from the same or a different species. Animal genes can be introduced into plants and vice versa. The gene will pass into subsequent generations, and this technique is therefore called 'transgenic'.

Genes can also be introduced into somatic cells which will replicate in the 'transfected' tissue, but will *not* pass into the germ cells. The somatic cells will die with the individual and the transfected gene will not appear in the progeny.

The gene for cystic fibrosis has been isolated and trials have commenced to introduce the normal gene by transfection to treat the disease by providing the missing enzyme that is the cause of cystic fibrosis. Haemophilia and other metabolic illnesses may be treated in this way. The gene may be introduced into the tissues by linking it to a harmless virus such as the adeno virus.

The examples that I have given are the beginnings of genetic engineering which at the moment are crude in its technique, but which without doubt will rapidly become far more refined. How can we ensure that this knowledge and the new techniques will benefit the environment and living creatures, including our own species? Vigilance will be needed to ensure that advances that initially appear attractive do not, with the passage of time, lead to harm. Western scientists have been alarmed by a draft law recently announced in China entitled 'Eugenics and Health Protection' which is designed to eliminate 'inferior births'. In the proposed law those with ailments such as hepatitis, venereal disease or mental illness, which can be passed on through birth, will be banned from marrying. The inherent dangers of political manipulation in the interpretation of this law are obvious.[24]

Our knowledge of molecular cell biology is increasing very rapidly and it is not at present possible to anticipate the likely developments even within a decade.

The dangers of applied genetics used politically to produce a 'master race' have already been mentioned. Aldous Huxley in *A Brave New World* anticipated the horror of breeding human beings, with defined characteristics having the intellectual and physical capabilities to create a society of maximum efficiency. The result was a 'loss of humanity' and the most important criteria that differentiate man from animals. An efficient society of 'bespoke bred' creatures, lacking charity, is a dreadful prospect.

What are the Possible Consequences of Genetic Engineering?

When the human genome project is completed we will know the coded arrangement of the human life process that bestows upon the new-born child its human nature, structure function and its deviations from normal congenital diseases and susceptibility to certain illness.

All of us have in our DNA harmful recessive genes some of which may be potentially lethal. For a couple with the knowledge that they both possess this harmful gene, the risk of their child manifesting the disease is 25% (see f*igure* 5). If they choose to ignore the danger, they may bring a doomed child into the world who may suffer grievously in the course of an inevitably fatal illness. Currently an affected foetus might be detected *in utero* and aborted. In the future it may be possible by genetic engineering to remove or replace the defective gene. Human genes have been inserted into plants and animals. Transgenic pigs with human

---

[24] *Nature* 1994 vol. 367 pp 1 & 3

genes are being bred in the hope that their organs may be acceptable as functioning grafts in man.

In *The Times* of 25 October 1993 there is a report of cloning a human zygote, causing two individuals to develop from one fertilised egg. The cloned individuals did not develop fully as they were abnormal. If this experiment is confirmed, then in theory it would be possible for artificially cloned individual embryos to survive. Deliberate selection of certain parental qualities could produce children of varying natural capabilities, physical, intellectual, moral and artistic. The stage would be set for a 'brave new world' with a sinister prognosis if the selection was politically motivated.

I have no doubt that the successful cloning of humans will occur and that far more specific and complicated genetic engineering of human and animal genomes will soon be possible. How can this inevitable progress be controlled? In most developed countries there are governmental regulatory authorities which produce guidelines and laws as to what types of experiments are permissible and how they are to be monitored. We know however that rules exist to be broken and human nature is not always programmed to pursue ethical activities.

Even without genetic engineering, but applying the knowledge of the genetics of tissue typing, some parents of children requiring bone marrow transplants have deliberately produced previously unplanned offspring to provide a well-matched brother or sister to give bone marrow to the afflicted child. There is a 25% chance of a perfect match. I would expect a similar line of thought and action to be followed when genetic engineering becomes repeatedly successful in human cloning. Then an ill individual could arrange for his or her clone to be produced to provide a vital organ for grafting. These speculations are only the tip of the iceberg of what will be possible by the application of genetic engineering. We must ensure that misuse is not made of these expected advances in biology. Decisions will not be easy. There is a great future potential here, either for good or for evil.

Sexual Reproduction: Individuals are Custodians of the DNA of the Species

The instinct to reproduce is programmed in the DNA of a fertilised egg and in the course of sexual reproduction, the progeny of a mating will have in each cell half the DNA from the mother and half from the father, so the dilution of the original parents' DNA will occur rapidly in each successive generation. However, the species DNA itself will still exist. The continued redistribution of nucleic acid genes with the invariable tendency to reproduce has been labelled 'selfish' by Dawkins in his book *The Selfish Gene*. This would seem to be an appropriate description of the behaviour. As far as man is concerned, there is a powerful sexual drive present in both sexes, and although the seeking out of a partner and the initiation of a sexual act is more likely to be instigated by the male than the female, this is not invariably the case. The drive is an extremely powerful instinct in all animals. The butterfly will find a mate by just smelling one or two molecules of the pheromone liberated by the female which may be more than a mile away. A male dog will search out a female through an extremely sensitive ability to detect and recognise the pheromone of a bitch on heat. In man, the sense of smell also exists attracting members of the opposite sex to each other when they are capable of mating, but specific attraction limited to a period of fertility is not a prominent feature in man.

Sexual attraction depends on physical appearance, personality and to a large extent, fashion. In Africa, the most attractive women are extremely fat by western standards, where an emaciated figure has, until recently, been regarded as the pinnacle of female beauty, often in a very tall girl. Most girls are not extremely tall or emaciated, the majority do not live up to the ideal, but if they did there would be no point in having an ideal. Similar characteristics apply to the male. A huge, athletic, intelligent, tender young man with perfect features is not to be found in every group of men. Both sexes that search for the ideal usually accept a compromise, settling for the attainable rather than the impossible. In the course of procuring a mate there are many other considerations besides sexual attraction. Is mating going to be accompanied by a legal contract and marriage? Will the partners work together after marriage? Do they each have a career? If they both work after marriage who will look after the baby? Whose career is most important? Does the family have money? Is there madness or other illness in the family? And in most countries, the first and foremost question is whether or not the proposed mate is of the correct religion, and if so, the right sect. With so many things to think about it is not surprising that there is so much rivalry, trial and error and breakdown of marital relations, when the prenuptial aspirations are not fulfilled. In the past, however, family considerations and religious and social taboos often kept an unhappy couple together, and it was expected of the children that they had a duty to look after their parents in old age. The concept of a united family, with generations living together and caring for each other, with mutual tolerance between different age groups, has changed markedly in the developed nations in the past fifty years. These considerations are still of paramount importance in many of the poorer countries, especially those dominated by fundamentalist religions.

To pursue a life devoted to the welfare of others has led certain individuals to reject material rewards. A vow of chastity is taken by both nuns and monks in several religions, and in India until recently, it was not uncommon for a widow to throw herself into the flames of her husband's funeral pyre to be united with him and receive his blessing. This practice of 'suttee' is now outlawed although occasionally still occurs in remote rural parts of India.

One example of overwhelmingly strong religious belief, which I have come across professionally, is the absolute refusal of Jehovah's Witnesses to receive blood transfusions, although they are quite prepared to receive organ grafts which will always contain some blood. There are many recorded examples of young members of this faith refusing blood and being supported in this by their closest relatives, who will watch them die for want of what is considered by most of the population to be a simple routine treatment. No amount of reasoning based on what is generally regarded as logic has any effect, nor would the offer of any kind of reward, since the patient and the family realise that death without treatment is inevitable. This is a tragedy for a doctor to witness, but of course is not aggressively directed at society.

A consideration of culture in the developed countries may be a source of satisfaction to the humanist from a secular point of view. The population is not increasing, and there is a tendency towards equality between the sexes in terms of opportunity to work, to earn money, and make decisions. Nobody in employment is hungry. But the divorce rate is high and many people do not even bother to get married, so the family is much weaker and threatened further. Old people no longer reside with the younger members of the family, despite the natural sympathy that often exists between grandparents and grandchildren. As soon as the elderly become decrepit either in mind or body, they are sent to residential homes where in their last few years they are unrelated to those caring for them. Social contacts are for the most part limited to others who are similarly aged and decrepit. They often seem to stare for hours at a television set without paying attention to the content of the programmes and sometimes without even noticing whether the set is switched on. This existence is a very sad ending for people who in their prime would have been vigorous, productive and interesting, with all the positive emotions that one expects of a healthy human being. In a civilised community, the care of the aged, the mentally disturbed and the physically handicapped must preserve the dignity of the individual, maintaining cleanliness in a gentle and compassionate environment. This is extremely expensive, it never produces a 'cure' and was a luxury not available until modern medicine prevented deaths from inter-current infection, particularly pneumonia.

For those without a job due to the failure of the economy or an inability to work due to poor education or defective personality, existence is also miserable. In most developed countries the unemployed are maintained with state handouts so that they do not starve, and efforts are made to house them, although some prefer to live rough. With such hopelessness, increasing unemployment and a meagre dole, it is not surprising that this underclass is tending to get larger in developed countries; they are unhappy, disaffected and often aggressive. Such individuals tend to become involved in drugs, crime and violence, although drugs, crime and violence are not confined to the underclass and may also be a temptation to those who are employed and are better off.

There are strong, aggressive, violent instincts in young males, probably in all countries, and these are certainly well demonstrated in northern Europe. Opportunities for venting their aggression often present themselves at football matches and other massed events. In the past, the constraints of religion and severe punishments were a deterrent, although they did not completely suppress the expression of gratuitous violence. Britain's temporary solution was to send such criminal individuals to penal settlements as far away as possible, Australia being an especially attractive choice because of its inaccessibility, once the American colonies were lost. This solution no longer exists, the 'hell-fire' power of religion has declined in developed countries, and punishments are far less severe, often having little in the way of deterrent value.

Another opportunity that presented itself frequently in the past to employ the aggression of young males was war, with compulsory military enrolment of men of appropriate age. The British Empire was largely created in this way. Now highly professional armies and air forces, requiring skilled operators and high technology, are necessary to handle the extremely dangerous weapons of modern warfare, and these are not suitable toys for mindless hooligans. The underclass is disaffected, angry and easily roused to anti-social behaviour, which is often violent. This is one of the main problems that all developed countries face.

If there is a preponderance of easily-recognised individuals of ethnic or religious groups who are different from the majority, then such communities can serve as a focus of hate for the rest of society. Variations on this theme seem to be the common factor in the tearing apart of the Balkan nations, especially Yugoslavia, and many of the individual republics that used to make up the Soviet Union. It is somewhat ironical that the European Union is exhorting the nations of western Europe to create a federal economy and a government with an enormous, expensive, inept and much-resented bureaucracy, whilst at the same time aspirations directed away from federalism seem to be the main concern of many nations. The bitter hatred of events in the past are well-remembered, sometimes going back hundreds of years and they provide arguments both in favour of, and against, federalism.

In the 1990s the term 'ethnic cleansing' has been used by people who were previously considered to be civilised. Between 1939 and 1945 millions of Jews were callously murdered by the Nazis because they were Jews. It is a dreadful warning to humanity that a brutal dictatorship, elected democratically, flourished in a nation with a long tradition of culture, especially in literature and music. Hitler was able to eliminate by mass murder Jews, gypsies, Jehovah's Witnesses, the physically and mentally handicapped, homosexuals, lesbians and anyone who objected to the Nazi regime. The 'pure' Aryan race was to be bred selectively according to the ideals of the Nazis, analogous to the methods used by horse breeders to obtain faster racehorses and by farmers to increase the milk yield of cattle. One can imagine what the Nazis would have done with today's knowledge of genetics. The millions who perished at the hands of the Nazis are a testimony to man's inhumanity to man and show how callous murder without compassion or pity degrades mankind to a level far below any behaviour observed in lower animals. The Holocaust Memorial in Washington is a fearful reminder of the weakness of human nature.

In this chapter it was seen that the sexual drive for reproduction is a universal characteristic, and that DNA appears to pursue its property of division, in terms of distributing genes into the next generation, in a highly targeted and selfish manner, selfish, that is, in relation to any other genes that might be competing. The individual human personality (or soul) exists in the brain and is a combination of inherited character and acquired experience. The traditional family, with three or more generations living together, persists mainly only in poor countries with powerful fundamentalist religions. In the West, family life is undermined by economic considerations, the search for pleasure, and a quest for independence and equality between the sexes. Those who are employed are for the most part contented, but current economic policies are based on weak theoretical considerations, and the market economy, subject to little control, is tending to destroy the environment and rape the planet. High technology seems to result in high unemployment in developed countries and unemployment is a major social evil that is dangerous to the fabric of society. In poor countries where the family tradition persists, the population is increasing; however the resources of food and its distribution will not be sufficient to cope with this exploding population. Starvation and armed conflict are ever-increasing evils, fired by the ethnic hatred of people with long memories for vengeance, and no thought of forgiveness. Hovering over us all the time is the threat of nuclear disaster, either by such weapons getting into the hands of maniacs or from accidental explosions of weapons or nuclear generating plants. Too much dwelling on these things could lead to depression. In the next chapter, I will consider some possible short-term remedies which could be implemented urgently and would probably have some beneficial effects.

Chapter 11

Short-term Remedies for Urgent Action

In earlier chapters I explained that the purpose of this book was to clarify the danger to mankind and the planet that the applications of science had caused when utilised by modern society, programmed by nature for a different kind of biological evolution. I suggested an analogy of a mega-tanker without a rudder heading for the rocks, but perhaps the analogy could be looked at in the modified form of a sailing ship, beautifully constructed of the best seasoned oak, with canvas sails and hemp rigging, into which has been fitted a modern diesel engine, invented as a result of the application of science and the workings understood by a few engineers. But the captain and crew of the ship have little understanding of the engine, of how to control it, and how to handle the ship which will behave very differently when propelled by a high-powered motor, rather than by the wind. The analogy is obviously far-fetched but there are features which seem to have an unpleasant relevance. Moreover, lack of communication and understanding between the captain and crew and the engineers can only lead to disaster.

An Understanding of Science

Unfortunately there has been little attempt by non-scientists to comprehend and communicate with science. It has been fashionable in certain academic environments for science to be ridiculed, and there have been errors of interpretation and mistakes in scientific deductions. However, the whole edifice of scientific knowledge rests on repeatability, and the facts that are deduced from experimentation, the observations made, their mathematical prediction and their successful application, is not an area for ridicule. The ability of politicians and businessmen to converse face to face in different parts of the globe within a day or two of travel rests on the jet engine and the modern airframe, or indirectly, immediately by telephone or fax. These are examples of applied science. In no way could the modern jet liner have been conceived and then brought to practical working reality without science. The same is true of the internal combustion engine, of all the modern, increasingly dreadful, weapons, and of almost all modern medicine and surgery.

In most educational systems the majority leave school with only a minimal understanding of science and the arts. In the common room of any major university the scientists may not have a full and detailed knowledge of the arts, but they often have some comprehension of the humanities and sometimes specialised expertise in particular art forms. Very few of the professors in the humanities could explain correctly the way in which biological characters are inherited, how the foetus develops and expand on the evolutionary theory, even in the most elementary terms. This ignorance of scientific matters among non-scientists, often proudly maintained, is unfortunate and could be disastrous to the world, especially since people in political power, no matter under what regime, are usually non-scientists. They may seek scientific advice to a varying degree but without sufficient understanding their utilisation of advice is often inadequate and inappropriate.

At the beginning of this book I pointed out the very simply-stated warning in the joint document of the Royal Society and The National Academy of Sciences. I am sure this document has been discussed by many committees, but it has never received anything approaching the importance and publicity it deserves. I doubt that many politicians understand it or are interested, and the public is ill-informed, unable to take a responsible view.

Teaching Science

A national basic science course that would be taken by all non-science graduates as part of their degree, would ensure that at least the language of science and the most important established concepts were part of the educational equipment of university graduates. This would include those aspects of biological science that have been mentioned above, and the mechanical, chemical, physical and mathematical sciences at a very simple level, especially emphasising the principles rather than the detail. The scientific method would be part of this course, explaining how hypotheses are conceived, experiments planned, the errors in experimental observation perceived, the analysis of observations and how they fit into the context of current theories. The dangers of errors of observation, of bias in interpretation and even fraud in scientific competition would be included. Most important is an explanation of how the use of science can be developed to construct and install mechanisms that work, such as air travel, railways, telephones and television. There should be an outline of modern medicine with emphasis on its powerful antibiotics, vaccination, anaesthesia, and advances that have caused a marked reduction in mortality of women in childbirth and in young children from infectious diseases. There would be a course on birth control and the dangers of the misappliance of science due to ignorance, greed or fecklessness and often a combination of all of these. It would also benefit the scientists to have a course on the basic humanities, covering ethics, politics, the history of religion and social anthropology. This broadening of education should allow members of the two separate cultures depicted by C.P. Snow[25] to talk to each other and perhaps improve society by mutual co-operation instead of the almost complete misunderstanding and mutual ignorance which exists in most developed countries. Courses in simple human biology should be available to children of all abilities.

There can be no argument about the success of science in terms of its technological achievement and its advances continue at an ever increasing rate. I feel, therefore, that there is a responsibility on scientists to use the same scientific method to prevent the catastrophe towards which we appear to be sailing. But scientists cannot do this without political and financial support. I fear that it is no use to expect effective action from individual nations although perhaps there is a sufficient

[25] C.P. Snow: *The Two Cultures & the Scientific Revolution*, 1959

long-term desire to survive amongst human beings to enable many of them to co-operate in a rational manner with a common goal. This would not even require altruism, but merely a survival instinct and a wish to save the lives of other creatures and plants on earth. The only political structure that might be able to act on a scale sufficiently large to make an impact is the United Nations. Unfortunately, much of the United Nations organisation seems to be preoccupied with bureaucratic circumlocution and the maintenance of good jobs, with security for those in high administrative positions.

Whenever one considers the different subjects raised in this book, the conclusion comes back with monotonous repetition that information and technology are available to avert the anticipated catastrophe, but that politicians of all persuasion are 'fiddling while Rome burns'. Partly because of the structure and apparatus of the political machinery in all nations, and partly because most politicians have no understanding of science and many are hostile to its achievements, although happy to use the fruits of it, for instance, jet travel, telephones and computers. A radical reorganisation of education would be an important and helpful start. Such courses have been introduced in some universities.

Economic Environmental Conflict

The aspirations of national economy and international trade do not fit in with the protection of the environment. Manufacturing countries and multinational companies wish to produce and sell more and more cars which will consume increasing amounts of fossil fuels. The petrol companies have always successfully blocked the manufacture of cars running on electric batteries. It is only when road congestion becomes so intolerable in cities like Los Angeles, Bangkok, Manila, Tokyo and London that eventually public opinion turns against the car, and then the motorist becomes an object of persecution. But poor public transport often gives the motorist no choice. There is nowhere to park, dreadful taxes and the feeling that he or she is a menace to society. Such persecution has been very well orchestrated against smokers in some western countries. This should reduce the incidence of arterial disease and lung cancer but there is now evidence that smoking diminishes the risk of developing Parkinson's and Alzheimer's diseases, both devastating chronic afflictions of the elderly.

To produce more food, precious forests are destroyed and not only will the trees be lost forever but also the myriad forms of animal and plant life that are associated with the rain forests will perish. Global warming from the greenhouse effect, a consequence of CO_2 production from burning fossil fuels, and the release of methane from grazing farm animals, seems likely to raise the level of the sea and cause flooding in many inhabited areas. Greedy and ill-considered farming, after a short, quick return of profits, leads to barren desert areas. The dangers of the nuclear alternative to fossil fuels have already been considered but the wind, the tide, the sun and volcanoes are all enormous sources of energy which modern technology could utilise if it was not so much more expensive than just burning irreplaceable fossil fuels and trees. The consumption of paper is another source of deforestation and here again the bureaucrats are especially guilty. Sir Rupert Hart-Davis [26] has pointed out that the Lord's Prayer contains 56 words, the Ten Commandments 297, the American Declaration of Independence 300, the European Economic Community Directive on the Export of Duck Eggs contains 26,911.

Most politicians are ignorant of, and indifferent or hostile to science, but instead of looking at medicine and science as dangerous and incomprehensible disciplines it would be more sensible to recognise that if applications of science are responsible for the mess we are in and the disaster that is likely to engulf us, then surely we should look to science to get us out of the mess and save the day. This implies that scientists must accept responsibility for their discoveries. Most scientists are intelligent and many of them have liberal humanitarian attitudes, so that when something is discovered which could obviously lead to terrible consequences, they are worried and some would even fail to reveal dangerous experimental observations feeling that, like Pandora's box, once opened it could never be closed.

It is certainly true that knowledge cannot be unlearned and the most strident example is nuclear energy. The usual motivation for scientific endeavour is curiosity, and the discipline involved in determining the nature of things is rigorous, repeatable and not open to argument once the data have been verified. Of course phenomena that are not understood will be the subject of speculation, hypotheses and theories that may or may not be correct. But the laws of energy, motion and gravity are for practical purposes irrefutable and their application is manifest in every day activity, for example, in the flying machine and the internal combustion engine. It is no use saying that science does not work, it clearly does. It is also equally erroneous to say that scientists know everything. In all areas of science that are of interest to those with original minds the answers are not clear and that is the reason why these subjects are being studied. For example we do not know the causes of most common cancers and arterial disease apart from the relationship to smoking. These two categories of illness are responsible for the majority of deaths in developed countries, although they tend to occur in those who are beyond childbearing age, and therefore they will not affect the population increase.

I feel that science education for everyone needs to be debated and would be of importance to all citizens in democratic countries, and hopefully one day for citizens of countries where free speech is at present not permitted. Democratic countries, as we have seen, have their own dangers, particularly since they are dependent on a free-market economy. Increasing the production of many goods consumes irreplaceable fossil fuels and forests, and fuel-using distribution is necessary to an expanding consumer community for the market to flourish. Those individuals who are not able to benefit from the economy in a democratic state will become impoverished, envious and antagonistic towards their more fortunate fellow citizens. Many will resort to crime, drugs and violence. These by-products of the market economy have so far defied all methods of control. The underclass

---

[26] Sir Rupert Hart-Davis — Author, editor and publisher, 1907-19—.

is getting larger and more dangerous in all large cities. It is only in the special environment of autocratic meritocracy such as Singapore, where it seems possible to have a thriving economy with happy citizens, no large underclass, and multiple religions and races living together in harmony, but of course a price has to be paid. Speech on most subjects is unrestricted but those who transgress the rules of society are treated harshly by the standards of western democracy, although not so by the standards of those dictatorships that are held together by armed force, police brutality and coercion.

Obviously the cure to our troubles is not going to be easy to find, but that is not a good argument for failing to try. In fact if we do not try, all will be lost in every kind of regime, political system, ethnic and religious group. Since it is clear to the savants of the Royal Society and the National Academy of Sciences that we are in trouble, it is incumbent on the rest of us to understand this and to ask the scientists for help in putting it right. Such a simplistic, optimistic hope may be regarded as quite naïve and this is sad because it is only by hoping to do well and striving to overcome our present inadequacies that we can live with modern science and technology and with our fellow creatures and the environment of this planet. In the next chapter I will try to look at ways in which the application of scientific knowledge and technology might be used to control population and prevent the continued destruction of animal and plant species, including ourselves.

Chapter 12

Long-term Goals

The Use of National Resource

Poor nations have little national resource for welfare and sadly the most populous nations with the greatest population growth spend much of their small 'kitty' on armaments, the political leaders fearing their neighbours or their own discontented citizens. Rich countries, and those aspiring to riches like South Korea, Taiwan, Malaysia and Thailand, are spending not only on their armed forces but also on schools and university education and investment in manufacture. The richer countries led by Japan are increasing the development of robotic manufacturing, which is cheaper and more reliable than human workers. Robotic minders need to be skilled technicians, therefore science, both 'pure' and 'applied', is a priority for state spending. Those whose jobs are taken over by robots will join the increasing number of unemployed. As the birth-rate drops in rich countries the proportion of the elderly in the community is rising. The collapse of the extended family, the tendency of substituting traditional marriage by sequential polygamy, and the scattering of family members geographically, means that there are increasing numbers of the elderly who must rely on the State for welfare.

Advances in medicine have been spectacular in the past sixty years but many of the new methods of effective treatment are expensive and do not always improve the quality of life. The United States of America spends 15% of its gross national product on health care, under which the insured can expect treatment of the highest standard, but the poor uninsured have inferior medical facilities, often in old hospitals. The overworked staff struggle with inadequate equipment in overcrowded and physically dangerous buildings where armed guards are on constant vigil to try to restrain the vendettas against people not yet killed in the drug-related street crime of the 'war zones'. 15% is a large slice of the national resources but it is not sufficient. Overheads of administration and the cost of implementing the insurance schemes accounts for large sums, up to 40% of the health care budget. Doctors pay enormous sums, some surgeons more than $100,000 a year, for malpractice insurance, an essential outlay since suing doctors is a popular pastime, encouraged by extraordinarily large settlements of damages given by the courts, persuaded in their generosity by the brilliant advocacy of malpractice lawyers who will receive 50% of the proceeds as 'contingency' fees. It is clear that the system is terribly wasteful and unfair on the poor and it is to the credit of the new administration that reform of health care is a major priority.

Just as applied science has unbalanced the population, so medical advances have outstripped the ability of even the richest nation to pay for all the medicine that is available. It is up to the politicians, whether democratically elected or acting in an autocracy, to provide the best care possible with the least wastage. Eventually in every country the bitter pill will have to be taken that the State of Oregon has already

Figure 15. Mrs Davina T, now seven years after the transplantation of the heart, lungs and liver

swallowed. In Oregon the State government has acknowledged that each nation can afford only a certain sum for the desirable 'cake' of health care and it has introduced a system of priorities to share out the cake. Inevitably some patients will be denied treatment, but it is better and kinder to withhold artificial kidney treatment from a patient of eighty incapacitated by a stroke, than fail to treat a child with acute appendicitis even if the former is rich and the latter poor. The next fifty years will present to every country increasingly complex problems about the distribution of their national resources to the competing claims from defence, police, prisons, welfare for the unemployed, the crippled, the mentally handicapped and aged, health care and education: not an easy task for anyone, especially when a political term of office is three to five years, or a potential successor has a knife poised over the back of a dictator.

How Valuable is One's Life?

Although a minority of humans usually fired with the fanatical zeal of fundamental religion and/or an ethnic cause appear to be quite happy to sacrifice themselves in the name of the cause, such heroic gestures are unusual. I have already cited the Tamil Tigers; the Kamikaze pilots in Japan are another well known example, young men who between eighteen and twenty years of age trained specifically for the purpose of flying a plane filled with explosives into the middle of an enemy target, usually a warship. They believed that this was their duty towards the emperor and the nation, and in fact it was an honour to be selected for this purpose. Most people, however, prefer to live and the wish to remain alive is very strong. I show an illustration of one of my patients who was referred to me for a liver transplant. She had cirrhosis, not due to alcohol. When we saw her we realised that a liver transplant was impossible because she also had lung disease and required continuous oxygen administration, and obviously she would not survive an anaesthetic. When this bad news was explained to her she said 'You must do something', and we said 'Well, there's nothing possible, since you have disease in the lungs and the liver, you would need transplantation not only of the liver but also of the heart and lungs.' She smiled and nodded and said 'Please would you do that.' In collaboration with our cardiac surgical colleagues we performed this enormous operation which previously had never been attempted and to our amazement she recovered quickly and with scarcely a hiccup in her health: she is now living the life of a normal housewife seven years later (*figure* 15). She is an extreme example of the will to live and the courage and fortitude to accept the risks of an operation that has not been done before, coming through with flying colours.

Unlocking Pandora's Box

These then are the two extremes of human attitudes to the importance of life: the Kamikaze pilots on the one hand and Mrs Davina T on the other. The overwhelming majority would prefer to cling to life and since this is the wish of humanity it is incumbent on those who make the decisions, namely politicians, to understand our predicament. As we have seen, the appalling outlook for the future is the result of the application of science. We must exhort scientists, who indirectly got us into this mess, to devise means by which humanity can live in a satisfactory balance with the rest of the creatures on the earth and not destroy the environment. Although we really do not know where we came from, why we are here or where we are going, no matter what speculations we choose to favour, the destruction of the planet we live in is unlikely to be an appropriate destiny for man unless one has a very nihilistic outlook on life. The best scientists are motivated by curiosity, trying to discover how things work and what are the relationships between different natural phenomena. When something new is discovered which has a potential for evil, such as atomic energy, scientists are worried. It is attributed to the nuclear physicist Leo Szilad, observing the first chain reaction of the splitting of the atom in Chicago in 1942, that he said: 'This will go down as a black day in the history of mankind.' Oppenheimer,[27] when he saw the test of the first atomic bomb, lamented, quoting from the ancient Hindu song of the Lord, the Bhagavad-gita, 'Now I am become death, the destroyer of worlds.' As the application of science becomes counterproductive to the ecology of the world, most scientists are exceedingly distressed and fully aware that man has now become like a cancer to the planet, and is in danger of destroying a great deal of living matter on the earth unless something is done. The warning of the Royal Society and the National Academy of Sciences shows that scientists are aware and feel responsible for what is happening. They would respond with enthusiasm to any exhortation by politicians, goaded on by public opinion in democratic countries, to seek methods of stopping the growth of this cancer, allowing Man to fulfil a role in a balance of give and take with the rest of the environment. Unfortunately, established individual political systems and ethnic and religious hatreds combine to frustrate a solution. Improvement will not be easy, quick or complete.

Does the mosaic of human society have sufficient goodwill and common sense to solve terrorism, crime, the problem of the urban underclass in developed countries, the weaknesses of democratic regimes and the repressive nature of dictatorial systems? What is necessary for the human race to survive and for individual human beings to live a dignified, peaceful and cultured existence? Are there Utopian solutions? Millions of people adhere to each of the main religions — Muslim, Buddhist, Hindu, Christian and Jewish, and the intensity of belief has in each case a range from almost secular to fanatic. Since the creeds are manifestly different and incompatible they cannot all be true. Nevertheless, there is a need that has been demonstrated throughout history, for established creeds associated with codes of behaviour which require certain characteristics of human nature to be controlled, and tolerance maintained, otherwise it is impossible for people to live together.

[27] Julius Robert Oppenheimer, American physicist, 1904-1967

Crime and Punishment

With conventional morality individuals vary in their readiness to transgress the established codes. For example, consider the ease with which an individual is provoked to aggression. Some disaffected individuals need no provocation and give vent to gratuitous violence and take pleasure in its execution. Envy and revenge may be strong provocations to murder and rape, the consequence of uncontrolled aggressive lust, but both violence and sexual assault may be features of a deranged mind.

At the other extreme of moral behaviour would be the saintly and altruistic, the unselfish devotion of a life's work to helping the poor, the sick and the weak, particularly those who dispense medical care, and hope and encouragement to the destitute living close to starvation in the slums of huge cities in underdeveloped countries. At each level of the spectrum there is a point of individual ethical decision. Most people in a civilised community will not steal, rape or murder, but some might be tempted to give false information to insurance companies or stay away from work claiming to be ill when they want another day to enjoy themselves. Each person has his own individual breaking point, but in a community with a strong fundamentalist religion carrying dreadful punishments for those who transgress and wonderful rewards for those who obey, the number of people accepting the given code of ethics in the community is likely to be much larger than in a free-wheeling democratic environment.

To be able to express one's views without fear of physical or social harm is a prize that most people in developed countries regard as priceless despite an associated high incidence of crime. There is a tendency in such communities for the punishment of offenders to become ever less severe, so that the police often complain that criminals who previously would never have resorted to violence, now carry arms and are prepared to use them to commit murder because the difference in punishment will not vary much in relation to the severity of the crime. There is continual spirited debate between those who feel that punishment should be a deterrent, as it certainly is in Singapore, and others who say that it has no such effect. For those whose threshold for breaking the moral code is very low, the use of guns and violence to facilitate crime is logical, provided the risks to themselves of being caught and severely punished do not seem to be too great. Such people used to be called evil: to them the arguments of liberal criminologists are a boon, which they seize cynically to exploit for their own benefit and the detriment of the community.

A Major Conceptual Change Will Take Time

Since major political reorganisation and change of attitude towards extreme dogma concerning birth control, and the protection of animal and plant life and the environment, are unlikely to occur quickly or spontaneously and could not be imposed on unwilling populations, effective action must be limited to what is possible. Financial pressure is probably more acceptable than other methods of coercion, and the destruction of irreplaceable fossil fuels and forests could be reduced by extremely high taxes, sufficient to persuade industry to turn to science to provide alternatives. For example, the widespread utilisation of 'clean' forms of energy from the wind, the tides, the sun and volcanoes could produce electricity on a large scale and with advances in battery technology the pattern of heating, cooling and transport could be transformed so as to reduce the present damage to the earth's resources. Electricity is already used for heating and cooling, but for land transport the use of petrol and diesel engines could be partly phased out, although for air transport, fossil fuels will still be needed. Electric cars could become the preferred option for ground travel if low taxation rendered them economical. The huge motor industry could be diverted to producing electrically powered vehicles.

The destruction of the world's forests has caused irreparable damage in many areas. The recycling of paper and minimising its use could also be brought about by taxation. In the course of a year many kilograms of paper are delivered to me, often in large envelopes. A generous estimate of the amount of this material that I read would be one per cent; the rest is of no importance to my work and consists largely of 'indigestible' bureaucratic garbage. Serious attempts could be made to use alternatives to paper, possibly re-usable plastic sheets or television screens for newspapers.

The above considerations are two approaches, based on taxation, which could easily be introduced in developed countries but would be more difficult in poor nations. Something will have be done to stop the rise in population, which is estimated at 1.7 million per week, or three a second world-wide. Individuals are brainwashed to possess numerous items of industrial production. In the developed countries the change in the pattern of life, particularly the widespread employment of women, has controlled population growth and in some countries the rate is even falling. The extreme urge to go forth and multiply seems to be submerged in the wish to enjoy life whilst it lasts and a large number of children is not conducive to a satisfactory professional working career for the mother and father. There is a tendency to consider traditional family life worth sacrificing but I suspect that this is a short-term, ill-considered move. It will be regretted in old age by those who have no children to take care of them. The alternative of a bureaucratic state to keep old people alive in an impersonal environment until some merciful catastrophe puts them out of their misery, is not attractive.

Patterns of mating, of choosing partners and even of monogamy may also change. The religious imperatives no longer exist to any wide extent in the developed world. In the United Kingdom thirty per cent of marriages end in divorce and the rate is increasing. If the human race is to continue and the birth rate be maintained, women are certainly necessary, but men only intermittently or perhaps not at all. A sperm bank or a few males reserved for mating could continue to sustain the human race in which the vast majority of the population were women. This could well be an advantage, since aggression is primarily a male trait dependent on male hormones circulating in the blood. In the one well-known exception to the rule of male dominance in mammals, the spotted Hyena, the dominant females have high circulating androgens and long penis/clitorises (see page 26).

The urge of individuals to reproduce, particularly of the male to impregnate as many females as possible, varies from species to species. In the preying mantis there is usually only one chance for the male and then, during the mating, the female proceeds to eat him. It is unlikely that this pattern would be a suitable role model in human society.

Control of population growth, although a worry for all mankind, is primarily a problem in the developing countries. How can it be contained? Education and improved methods of traditional birth control are approaches that we understand, and they would probably have much more success if they were more vigorously pursued with much greater funds. New methods of 'depot' birth control injections or implant which will prevent fertilisation for several years are under trial but widespread use would require education, an efficient distribution arrangement and acceptance by the government and by religious leaders that birth control is desirable. Perhaps pecuniary incentives would help those who limit their family to two and higher taxes for those who insist on having large families.

The Right to Reproduce

In previous chapters I have argued that living in a civilised manner in both an urban and a rural environment must, of necessity, incur certain rules and regulations in order to prevent chaos and anarchy. The basic requirements are to prevent murder, rape, theft and other crimes of violence, but with each development of community life new laws become essential. For example, the need to levy taxes to remove garbage, run schools and hospitals and maintain the roads. The privilege of using the roads requires further regulations which are regarded as reasonable by responsible citizens: for example the need for a minimum driving age and a test before one is permitted to drive a car, as well as the avoidance of high levels of alcohol and other drugs in the blood while in charge of a potentially lethal vehicle.

To bring a child into the world is a serious responsibility and most people would regard it as feckless and anti-social to bear a child if one has no immediate or foreseeable means of supporting the child, so the infant is a burden on the tax-paying community, which may last for many years. We have seen that the urge in man to mate is as powerful as in animals, and sterile mating, when there can be no possibility of conception, is an unusual mammalian behaviour limited among the primates to man and the pygmy chimpanzee. In a world which is rapidly becoming over-populated, with an industrial economy that seems to be unable to support full purposeful employment in any nation, there is a strong case for rules limiting the number of births. It would not be unreasonable, by analogy with a motor vehicle licence, that a permit to reproduce should also be needed with a minimum age of, for example, twenty-five, and a proof required that the parents are of sufficient maturity and financial resource to take proper care of the child. Young, sexually active, but emotionally immature teenagers would need help. Counselling could be supplemented where necessary by 'depot' type contraceptives which could be given from the age of puberty and if a similar contraceptive could be developed for males, then recreational sex would not be accompanied by a penalty to society involving the young parents of an unwanted child that they cannot look after.

The Aggressive Unemployed Men

In any large city there is likely to be a small minority of people, usually young males, who are aggressive by nature, participate in crime and appear to have no moral conscience that is in any way sympathetic to the general feelings of the community. Such a person whom we call an 'enemy of the people' is unlikely to be cured of his affliction by imprisonment or for that matter by any other punishment. If, however, he is seen to be able to get away with his crimes with relatively minor punishment this can become an important encouragement to others to follow a life of crime. Most intelligent people who may have innate anti-social aspirations would nevertheless repress them and behave in a civilised manner if they felt it was likely that their crimes would be discovered and they would be severely punished. I believe that this deterrent effect exists despite the many protestations of sociologists and liberally-minded criminologists, but I also believe that a very strong case can be made for trying to direct the energies of a potential criminal away from an easy life of theft and violent behaviour that threatens his fellow citizens. Towards this objective, the provision of more jobs, and the opportunity to participate in athletic sports can be helpful, although this ideal is much more easily stated than put into practice.

For a world-wide adoption of population control using established methods, the United Nations would seem to be the only body that could lead an effective campaign, but considerable resources would be needed. Unfortunately, there may not be very much time in which to produce the changes of attitude which traditionally require prolonged negotiation and patience. I have suggested that since the application of science has got us into this mess, science should be charged with the responsibility of a solution. In the next chapter I will consider some ways in which modern medicine and science could be put to this task.

Chapter 13

A Scientific Approach to Control of Population — A United Nations Laboratory for Population Studies

In the preceding chapters I have looked at population demography, at animal and human behaviour and biology, at religion and politics, with the inevitable conclusion that we have to live with our destructive human nature but still try to face the reality of our plight. We need to stop the rape of the earth and our own forthcoming destruction by harnessing every possible horse to pull the human disaster coach away from the cliff edge. That means recognising that only by the practical and immediate application of all branches of science can we reverse the disasters that have resulted from a blinkered short-term exploitation of science in the recent past and the continuing present. It will require supreme efforts of mankind and all its institutions.

We have seen that conventional morality, religious beliefs and political systems were not seriously at variance with the existence of a relatively stable population until powerful new methods of killing enabled those nations with the most lethal weapons to dominate the rest. The developed nations brought scientific medicine to their colonies, thereby reducing the previously very high death rate from infectious diseases in children, and in women in childbirth. The naturally evolved reproductive potential of women, which was appropriate to a high infant, childhood and maternal mortality, became unbalanced and it has remained so, which is the main cause of the population increase. Would it be possible to change the female reproductive potential in a harmless manner so that the balance was restored or alternatively, could male fertility be controlled to the same effect? A careful look at both these possibilities would provide a *prima facie* case for serious scientific investigation. Since there are billions of sperms produced for each fertilised egg, but each woman only has 50,000 mature ova, of which only a small fraction can be fertilised in the interval between puberty and the menopause, it might be easier to obtain a change in fertility through the female, but manipulation of both the male and female could be possible.

If we look at the mechanisms, the directions of research are clear. Already we have powerful drugs that will change the internal environment of the body; long-acting slow-release contraceptive agents similar to the 'pill' but injected, and effective for five years, have been used to facilitate the control of contraception when the taking of a pill cannot be relied upon due to poor environmental conditions or low intelligence in the population concerned. Female sterilisation by Quinacrine pellets inserted into the cervix is more acceptable than tying the fallopian tubes, which requires an operation. There are certain agents that will have a similar effect on the production of sperms in the male but the more easily applied method for the male is to perform a vasectomy which interrupts the tubes along which the sperms are conveyed to the exterior. This operation is simple, quick and cheap but to all intents and purposes it is permanent, because reversing the procedure is difficult and uncertain. A more discrete manipulation, in which the actual programming of the reproductive cells could be changed, would be something to consider in the more distant future.

It would be conceivable (a rather unsatisfactory word) to introduce a vaccine by means of a virus vector, to change the behaviour of the oocyte or the cells that control it. Ideally, this vaccine would be unharmful to other parts of the body and would not be activated until after the second pregnancy. In case a disaster happened, such as an accident to one of the children, it might be desirable for there to be a method to inhibit the contraceptive action; and perhaps this could be achieved by hormonal treatment that could override the inhibitory effect. Experimental virus vaccines to control fertility in males and females are now being developed. The difficulty, as with all the methods that have been mentioned, would be the distribution and administration of the vaccine, especially in poor communities, since fundamentalist religious views would be likely to oppose any such action. To control the size of world population effectively would not meet with the approval of any United Nations organisation unless the crescendo of disasters that seem to be developing had reached a much more critical stage, by which time it could well be too late to avoid the major catastrophe of the overwhelming immigration of poor, starving, overpopulated communities into the prosperous western countries and the accompanying danger of strife, bloodshed and possibly the unleashing of nuclear weapons.

A more acceptable method of establishing a control of family size would be by education and economic pressure. It is very unlikely that there would be any strong desire on the part of developed countries, enjoying a high standard of living and with no increase in their own population, to sacrifice their quality of life in order to feed, house and keep warm communities that were increasing their population in a feckless manner. But in these same developed nations one sees huge automobiles with a single occupant, excessive food consumption and a gross wastage of heating and cooling energy; these will eventually need to be abolished with strict enforcement to curtail the mindless greed and profligacy of many rich people. The rich western countries could make the availability of effective birth control a condition for giving financial and technological aid to underdeveloped overpopulated nations, while curtailing their own consumption and wastage.

Most governments of developing nations realise that the increase in their population is impoverishing their citizens and that even in countries that are firmly in the grip of fundamentalist regimes, the leaders must still be able to recognise the poverty consequent on the increasing population. The invasion of neighbouring nations would have been the traditional solution, but this is now unacceptable because of the terrible weapons available for defence and attack. It is likely therefore that a safe and effective method of controlling the population will in general soon be welcomed, or at least become acceptable to most nations where the increasing population is a major problem. New effective 'depot' injectable contraception could be distributed by the wealthy nations, and economic help could go hand in hand with evidence that effective steps were being taken to control the number of new births. Thus food, technology and the sharing of applied science could all be linked to a determination to stop the population explosion. No method apart from persuasion linked to economic help would be acceptable and effective, since the urge to limit the population appears to come only from the wealthy developed nations imposing on those who are less fortunate.

Per capita, individuals in rich nations are far more destructive of the environment than the citizens of poor countries. An honest and determined effort to reduce the profligacy of Western Europe and North America is a large and essential part of any programme to limit the population and stop the rape of the earth.

I have written this book in the hope, rather than the expectation, that serious notice will be taken of the warnings which, as I have tried to explain, are the received judgement of the most august scientists and scientific bodies. Science has been attacked from many directions, particularly by those ignorant of what it means. There is no agreement on the answers to the questions 'Where have we come from?', 'Why are we here?' and 'Where are we going?' in the main religions; each has a different view. I would assume that the lack of common ground indicates that the answers are not known in the usual sense of the word and belief and faith in the individual creeds is not testable. Clearly, members of the Hindu religion will not accept the explanations given by the Muslims and vice versa.

The faith required to accept scientific truth is of a different nature because it is testable. The theory of what power of engine would be needed in a given design of an aircraft size, weight and shape in order for it to fly, may or may not be correct, but the veracity can be tested and the method clearly works in view of the usually successful take off and landing of modern aeroplanes. The same is true in modern medicine, based on scientific biology. A staphylococcus that can be cultured from the blood would invariably be fatal in all previous experiences of the condition, but by giving the patient an antibiotic in the correct dose that will kill the staphylococcus, the patient will survive. This is a very easily repeatable observation and no sane person would dispute the connection between the antibiotic and the survival. The same certainly is known of the number of potential individuals that could be fertilised in terms of the number of eggs each woman produces in her fertile lifetime and this is a gross over-production compared with what she is physically capable of in terms of supporting pregnancy. The over-production of sperm is far more excessive still and apparently wasteful. These observed facts and the extreme reduction of maternal, perinatal and child mortality are obvious explanations of how the massive increase in world population has come about. The tendency towards conflict and aggression in different human societies, especially when based on religious and ethnic origin, is self evident, but presumably could be accepted and controlled with education.

The application of this approach is the only way in which we can stop the insupportable population increase endangering the human species and all other animal and plant species as well, indeed as the whole environment of the planet. Unless we recognise that over-population is a malignant growth on the earth there will not be sufficient resolve to institute effective treatment and the growth will have a disastrous effect. There are methods by which treatment could be given but whether they are compatible with the frailties of human nature in the entrenched, fanatically-held beliefs of a large portion of human society, is an open question, the answer to which we will presumably have available in the next hundred years. Let us hope that the rational, loving and compassionate side of human nature overcomes the ignorance, greed and aggression which is the dark side of human personality.

Population Control: The Most Urgent Task for the United Nations

The purpose of this book is to alert the public and politicians that the threat to humanity, to other living creatures and to the resources and environment of our planet is real. The prospects of disaster are not remote in time but are already occurring and rapidly accelerating. Applications of science, many of which would appear to be laudable in isolation, are in fact responsible for our troubles. If the world population could be contained or reduced instead of increasing at the present rate of one billion per decade, then the imbalance that now exists between man and the rest of the world could probably achieve a new and more benign equilibrium. If we fail to grasp the nettle now, involuntary population control will result from the disagreeable prospect of famine, conflict and probably a major nuclear disaster. Since 'grasping the nettle' is difficult, and in the short -term unpopular and possibly dangerous to their careers, it is eschewed by most politicians. Individual nations can look at the world scene and if sufficiently enlightened and altruistic, put their own houses in order, diminish or abolish the use of fossil fuels, the destruction of forests and the profligate waste of water. Education can be improved, so that bearing children without being able to look after them emotionally or financially ceases. Such measures directed towards achieving a local utopia are of little help globally if the opposite policies are adopted by most other nations. Moreover, the utopian state depicted above would be a source of extreme envy for the disaffected inhabitants of feckless nations, the poor unemployed, uneducated, hungry and aggressive. To prevent being overrun by these dangerous and unacceptable potential immigrants, 'Utopia' would have to invest in a powerful defence force and having an excellent scientific base, they would produce the most effective killing machines: nuclear weapons. There can be no doubt that faced with their own destruction, Utopians would reluctantly feel forced to use these weapons. This scenario in the past has been enacted countless times all over the world with only local consequences: the sacking and burning of a village or city, but now the killing potential is so terrible that the use of nuclear weapons would have far reaching and devastating effects on the rest of the planet even if the probability of a chain reaction by other nations of pre-emptive strikes and retaliation did not occur.

Since local reversal of the rape of the earth by individual nations is highly desirable but will have limited global consequences, what effective options are available? The United Nations, although a much criticised organisation, is a forum which can look at and react to international disasters. The considered views of the UN, often couched in obscure 'politically correct' compromise terms, nevertheless are respected by most nations. The UN has devoted funds towards scientific matters dealing with health, including reproductive health, the prevention of famine, and it has responded to natural and man-made disasters, but to date the major problems facing us because of increased population have not been addressed in an objective and logical manner with sufficient urgency. The lobbying and obstructions of religious and national bodies and institutions have prevented an honest confrontation with the dilemma: we must either control population by the humane method of birth control or face the consequences of the chaotic and dreadful killing of humans and other creatures, which will reduce the world population in a manner unacceptable to even the most powerful opponents of contraception. Just as scientists in the Second World War were charged with producing in a few months the most dreadful weapon ever conceived, and other scientists were later directed to placing a man on the moon, both formidable achievements, so should the UN provide the funds and the organisation for active scientists to investigate all the aspects of the population problem and devise ways of coping with this potential disaster in an humane and sensitive manner.

Co-operative Action

If only there could be established a scientific division of the United Nations, headed by a scientist with the administrative capacity of Lee Kuan Yew, to use scientific methods to work out means of controlling the growth of population, to stop the rape of the earth and minimise the dangers of a nuclear war! It would need to be a non-political, non-religious body, similar in concept to the Royal Society and the National Academy of Sciences, able to speak the truth rather than indulge in the lies of politically correct statements or the prevarications of politicians. Such a UN science division would need a strategy of long-term planning with targeted research aimed at the objectives mentioned above. Perhaps the common goal of self-preservation, if the reality and the urgency could be made apparent, would enable the individual nations to co-operate in such an endeavour and make sure that executive action followed the scientific investigations.

Of course scientific data and the practical proposals emanating from these data would be quite impotent if there were no political implementation. But there is a recent, somewhat heartening, precedent for the United Nations being able to act effectively and successfully in kerbing tyrannical behaviour and in helping to distribute food to the starving. The goodwill of most nations, certainly of the most powerful nations, would be needed, but the spearhead would inevitably be formed by the most scientifically advanced nations with established scientific bases and institutions, those that are seeking an understanding of nature, including human nature. Modern science is demonstrably effective in unravelling mysteries by experimental methods that can then be repeated by independent colleagues. Unfortunately the development of new scientific discoveries has often been disastrous, especially in the production of nuclear weapons, but also inadvertently in unbalancing nature by preventing a high level of childhood and maternal deaths and by removing selection by evolutionary pressures on survival, thereby changing the wastage of natural biological over-fecundity.

A permanent scientific laboratory with continuous contact between working scientists and executive government would be a step in the right direction. The institution would need to be run by active scientists without a bureaucratic supra or infrastructure. Although the United Nations have scientific, technological and medical branches, they tend to be run by bureaucrats and only have indirect contact with scientists who are actually 'working at the bench'. This is a dreadful weakness, which must be corrected.

In every nation bureaucracy has an inexorable tendency to reproduce itself in a similar way to the sexual drive of living creatures. The pattern of bureaucratic progeny is to produce an ever increasing number of committees, and sub-committees, models of complexity which can only be dealt with by further complexity. The system provides, as Parkinson[28] has analysed very skilfully, an hierarchical structure, the chiefs becoming more and more powerful, with increasing staff absorbing funds at an alarming rate, and in general there is an inverse relationship between the number of bureaucrats and the efficiency of the system. Even a superficial consideration of the health service arrangements in any developed country will show how the bureaucratic system eventually expands to a state of almost complete constipated inactivity, where the only semblance of labour is of bureaucrats talking to each other, often losing sight completely of the basic *raison d'être* of their employment, which, in the case of the health service, is the patients.

The scientific wing of the United Nations, to be effective, would require participation from active scientists available in all branches of scientific endeavour who would help and would have the power of decision together with the United Nations politicians, in the use of science and technology to try to prevent the continuing rape of the earth, by sanctions and military force if necessary. Because of the established separate national political systems, and even more importantly, the negative power of orthodox religious beliefs, a consensus from the United Nations on any subject has always been extremely difficult to achieve, and there have been some dissenters in every major decision. In recent years powerful armed action on behalf of the United Nations has given respect to the muscular side of this organisation, mainly thanks to the technological superiority of American weaponry and the resolve of individual politicians to carry a task out to its completion.

A similar approach to the ecological dangers brought about by the expanding world population would be possible, not only in education about birth control, but also in providing the means whereby contraception can be made available. Help should be given to farming communities in the use of mechanised farming which reduces the labour requirements and makes the need for a large family, particularly of sons to do the work on the land, no longer an overwhelming priority. Religious fundamentalism is unlikely to accept any kind of logical argument for change, but education in developing countries has resulted in many individuals going their own

---

[28] C. Northcote Parkinson: *Parkinson's Law or the Pursuit of Progress*

way on birth control, especially in communities that are becoming more affluent. For those that are underfed in an unstable economy the outlook is grim, and the desolation produced by civil war, and the terrible degradation of humanity resulting from famine, have only too often become the norm in many different places but especially in equatorial Africa.

The Laboratory for Population Studies

Any proposal involving a huge organisation such as the United Nations is liable to built-in inertia with a stranglehold of bureaucratic inefficiency characteristic of all large institutions. These matters are of central concern and could be the death knell of a viable 'Laboratory of Population Studies'. The siting for a laboratory and its funding should not present serious difficulties, but the recruitment of scientists, and the structure of the laboratory in terms of hierarchy, would need very serious attention. I have suggested that to be of any value the scientists working in the 'Laboratory of Population Studies' should all be active, working scientists who are strongly motivated to try to prevent the rape of the earth and the destruction of mankind. I doubt if there would be difficulty in recruiting the right talent provided the laboratory was seen from the outset to be a genuine humanitarian scientific enterprise. In order to recruit the best brains in each discipline, the appointments should be for one or two years, rather like a sabbatical post, so that the scientists could return to their own laboratories after contributing to the UN laboratory. There would be a good reason for the laboratory to be established close to a major area of population increase: New Delhi might be especially suitable because the Indian Government recognises the gravity of the situation and is committed to act positively. There are precedents for highly successful, non-hierarchical laboratories, the laboratory for Molecular Biology in Cambridge, and the Basle Institute for Immunology being obvious examples with justified outstanding reputations, but these are both devoted to narrowly defined fields of study. The proposed UN Laboratory would need to be multi-disciplinary but with a minimal and very light-handed administrative structure. An hierarchical institute would frighten good scientists away defeating the whole object of the exercise. The topics to be studied would include those covered in this book, namely:

1. Population demography world wide
2. The biology of human reproduction
3. New methods of birth control
4. Human nature, politics, religion and prejudice relevant to population demography
5. Food resource
6. Mineral and water resource
7. The destruction of animal and vegetable species by man
8. The consequences of spreading high technology for short term economic gain and ways to stop this legally

9.   World-wide unemployment and pressures for emigration
10. Dangers of national, racial and religious conflict
11. Crime and punishment. The dangers of civil disorder with an increasing
     population of deprived unemployed, aggressive young males
12. The increasing elderly population and how to look after the chronic sick.

The Laboratory for Population Studies would be charged with total and effective responsibility and a need to respond in all the areas enumerated above. It would be expected to make recommendations as to how the rich developed world can help poor nations, without aggravating their troubles, how religious fundamentalist leaders can be persuaded of the futility of prohibiting the control of family size, how to encourage small families world wide and, above all, the actual means by which birth control can be provided without penalty, and free, for those individuals who wish to use it. These would be the general topics; the specific approaches would need to be addressed in the accepted manner of scientific investigation. There would not be much point in having this laboratory unless the United Nations took note of its findings and recommendations and acted speedily, with sufficient authority and funds world-wide to be effective.

   The interaction between national and UN politicians, and the scientific community involved in this laboratory, would need to be cordial and delicate, not an easy objective in view of what we know of human nature, but unless the need for action of this type is appreciated there may well be no human nature left. Those working in the laboratory should have an effective platform to explain what they want to do and be forceful advocates for these plans of action.

   Although the bureaucracy of the UN might have difficulty in reacting to the task of creating a 'Laboratory of Population Studies', there is no shortage of scientists of outstanding ability who are passionately concerned by the population explosion. The documents of the Royal Society and the American Academy of Science and the Signatories of *Warning on Population and Global Deterioration* are a source of intellectual wealth from which a small multi-disciplinary team could be recruited. Specialists in reproductive physiology, contraception, animal and plant ecology, the atmosphere, oceans, fossil fuels, bio-engineering, nuclear energy, economics and human behaviour should form a nucleus of the task force to advise the UN on what is wrong and strategies to remedy the interconnected complex troubles that plague us in an age of applied science that is mismatched to our inherited biological programmes. This should be the think-tank of think-tanks, with power to implement.

   This first step in recognising and responding to the human tendency to 'self destruct' could place the ball firmly in the court of the UN to attempt, by peaceful means, to implement the recommendations of the population laboratory. The production of a long-acting safe and reversible contraceptive would provide an appropriate tool, but its use would require explaining to the nations reluctant to control their populations, that to turn their backs on the offer would incur disaster for themselves and the planet. This global argument would need to be reinforced by economic aid on a huge scale given by the rich nations to the poor countries and to the underclass in their own cities; directed and supervised so that the money is spent wisely on education, on the enthusiastic and effective implementation of birth control, and on provision for the training of scientists to improve the quality of life for the millions living on the verge of starvation in filth and despair. This means that the most influential scientists of each nation, those whose responsibility is to advise the appropriate ministries, must be lobbied and recruited to pressure their governments and the UN. This should not be too difficult as such bodies as the Royal Society, and others mentioned in the preceding pages, are already urging their members to become more active. Individual effort must be replaced by joint effort. The scientific and medical community, if united, has many weapons at its disposal and constitutes a powerful lobbying force.

Inevitably the rich will have to sacrifice many of its luxuries, such as the excessive heating and cooling of buildings, and the use of multiple cars that they currently consider essential. The uncontrolled dumping of manufactured goods, of bio-engineered food and the proliferation of weapons, especially firearms, aggravate social discontent, increasing unemployment and the tendency for young frustrated males to become criminals, a recipe for global disaster. There can be no doubt that the task of the proposed population laboratory, and a positive and effective response by the UN and by individual nations, will be difficult to achieve, time consuming and beset with many disappointments, caused by the vagaries and selfishness of human nature and the entrenched positions of religious and fundamentalist political regimes, but unless we can succeed in persuading mankind that continuing in our present course will be disastrous for *everyone*, we cannot hope to avert catastrophe. I believe it is just possible that persistent logical argument, backed by joint action, acceptable to the majority of rational human beings might succeed in promoting an application of 'Salvation Science' on a scale that would rescue our species and other living beings from a dreadful fate. *Now* is our last chance to avert the catastrophe that is hanging over us. Should a local disaster occur, as it surely must, we must use its occurrence as a spur to immediate action.

Chapter 14

Practical Considerations

I have looked at the warnings of the population explosion and have attempted to analyse the causes, consequences and the extreme danger of our predicament. The need for a scientific solution has been argued, and the best way in which this could be achieved would depend on international collaboration and the establishment of a non-hierarchical Laboratory of Population Studies as defined in the previous chapter. What are the real chances of such a laboratory being established? If it was built and staffed how would we prevent it being rendered impotent by bureaucracy? A chauvinistic sharing out of resources and the appointment of tame scientists, subservient to short-term national interests, would be a disaster. The distinction, competence and independence of the scientists appointed should be the only criteria of assessment, irrespective of their nationalities. They should have a real commitment to the total world situation.

The laboratory that I have in mind would be in the form of an institute with different individual departments looking at each aspect of what has been considered in this book. The recommendations of the institute would then be available for implementation by the United Nations. Certain divisions of the United Nations, particularly the World Health Organisation, would naturally be involved in the practical applications of recommendations from the Laboratory of Population Studies. A central executive role by the United Nations would also be required since finance, technology, food supplies and political interaction would be needed. The scientists might be quite clear in their minds as to what should be done, but this in no way guarantees that politicians nationally and internationally would listen to them, nor will unpalatable recommendations sway the prejudice of religious leaders unless the seriousness of failing to act is stressed. Predictable disasters that occur will make this possible.

Bearing in mind the discussion in earlier chapters on the frailties of human nature, it is unlikely that the United Nations will act with sufficient resolution until far more serious catastrophes have occurred directly attributable to population growth. This is dangerous and worrying but by no means unlikely. Unfortunately the longer it takes for corrective action to be started the less likely is a successful outcome without terrible loss of life and human suffering. We must take advantage of small disasters to prevent larger ones.

There is amongst most young people a strong wish to preserve nature and not to damage the environment. Perhaps a mobilisation of this dynamic 'green' attitude in a practical way would compel hard-bitten politicians to focus on the population explosion before too many more people suffer. If these matters were taught and debated in schools it would provide democratic countries with considerable lobbying force for individual national governments. This could be translated into international co-operation by the United Nations.

The proposed scientific solution might require private finance and national funds to establish a Laboratory for Population Studies. The UK Department of Overseas Development has already allocated funds towards human population studies. The Clinton Administration has given \$13.2 million to the International Planned Parenthood Federation and has resumed funding for the United Nations Population Fund. National scientific academies could be expected to endorse this development. The many concerned scientists throughout the world who have signed the warning referred to at the beginning of this book, should support the establishment of sabbatical posts in the various disciplines listed in the last chapter to work in a Laboratory for Population Studies. Experimental laboratory work would investigate safer and more acceptable methods of long-term contraception. Fieldwork would determine how human nature and age-long prejudices could be reconciled with what has to be done to limit the number of children in communities with an excessive birth-rate. According to Potts,[29] the wish for family planning is strong in the populations which are most in need, and he states:

> The demand exists, the technology is available and the cost of making family planning universally available by the year 2000 is trial in relation to other global issues.
>
> Global population increases by one million more births than deaths every 100 hours — a new Glasgow every four days, or a new Los Angeles every 12 days. The world is on a knife edge. The policies set today can easily raise or lower the final stable population of our planet by several thousand million. Hundreds of millions of people in the developnig world wish to plan their families although they cannot afford the full price of modern technologies.
>
> The most successful family planning services offer informed, voluntary choices in culturally appropriate, easily accessible ways.[30] Specifically, they:
> - provide contraceptives at numerous locations
> - sell contraceptives at acceptable prices
> - deliver oral contraceptives without a doctor's prescription
> - offer male and female sterilisation without limits of age or parity
> - maintain long periods of breast feeding
> - deal with the public health problems associated with unsafe abortion.

A financial advantage offered to those limiting the size of their families should be part of our strategy to overcome the prejudices against contraception. I believe that with appropriate education and debate there could be sufficient understanding and good will to act as I have suggested. I am optimistic that it will be possible, but it is likely to be a close run thing. It will be sad if progress has to depend on a dreadful catastrophe to concentrate the minds of our political masters, but if it happens, the opportunity must not be wasted.

[29] Unmet Demand for Family Planning, *Interdisciplinary Science Reviews* 1993, vol. 18 no. 2
[30] M. Potts and A. Rosenfield: 'The fifth freedom revisited', *The Lancet*, 1990, 336, pp 1227-31

EPILOGUE

Man Cannot Live By Bread Alone

In this short book I have tried to look at the human condition objectively, clearly an exercise in wishful thinking since selectivity and bias cannot be excluded. The difficulties that bar the way to reversing the decline in our relationship with the environment are enormous and we cannot change the human nature imprinted in our DNA. Merely to exist with sufficient food and shelter is the aspiration of humans deprived of these necessities, but once these are satisfied the mind is free to focus on other things. A severe pain will similarly exclude all other considerations, and only when the pain has been eased is it possible to carry on with normal activities. Once relieved of acute stress, the next priority of humans and most other species is to reproduce so that the human genes continue to survive.

The environment that humans seek in which to nurture their DNA has changed almost beyond recognition from the *modus vivendi* of the early human tribes. Modern cities, with electricity for light and heat, public and private transport, labour-saving appliances, mass world-wide communication and the most dreadful machines designed for the destruction of life are all taken for granted, and are the creations of science. As we have seen, these hallmarks of modern civilisation are not compatible with the uncontrolled population increase. If the growth of population is unchecked, bloody conflict will not be preventable.

The contrasting facets of human nature vary from the complete, selfish and often violent disregard of others, to selfless compassion. We admire heroes in whatever fields are fashionable, bravery in combat, martyrdom for a cause, skill in literature, painting, sculpture, the performing arts, and the prevention of suffering by modern medicine. Less noble but more popular now are the heroes of television and pop music because they are visibly successful. In the West freedom is greatly admired, of speech, action and religion, but uncontrolled freedom leads to anarchy: a dangerous situation in which the weak, the old or those identified as in some way different are persecuted. When freedom is curtailed and laws are strictly enforced, there is civil discipline and the streets are safe. It is hard to find a middle path in which freedom is cherished and civil behaviour follows the creed of 'live and let live'.

Unless we acknowledge the dangers of our present course and apply scientific method to control the population, man will not long be able to indulge in the luxury of civilised living and may not continue to survive at all.

Figure 16. 'Science: The Fruit of the Tree of Knowledge' by Roy Calne.

Courtesy of The Science Museum, London

HYPOTHESIS (*figure* 16)

The Creator's Testament to Modern Man

I have given you DNA programmed by evolution through millions of years. It has form, function and instincts derived from your anthropoid ancestors. You have evolved the gift of language and intelligence to possess the ability to reason, to enquire, to have abstract thoughts from which you may experience rich emotions. These blessings bestowed on you are to be used to live in peace with fellow-men, animals, plants and the elements of the earth.

From your ancestors you have inherited the urge to reproduce to preserve your precious DNA. Many of the secrets of nature are now revealed to you by your probing curiosity and rational analysis. This knowledge can be used for good or evil.

The legend of the serpent who gave Eve the fruit of knowledge is a terrible warning; beware not to succumb to the temptations of greed, envy, fanatic hatred and lust for power to dominate others. If you continue to multiply without constraint or consideration of the rest of the world you will swiftly exhaust irreplaceable resources, animal, vegetable and mineral, which will surely lead to the destruction of your DNA and the desolation of the planet.

You will have many hard decisions to make but I have given you the ability to choose. In the spirit of love and compassion towards your fellow men and all living creatures, animals, and plants, use your scientific knowledge to choose and act wisely to devise ways of sharing without exploitation, to live and let live.

I hope you become *Homo SAPIENS*, the alternative is *Homo EXTINCTUS*.

I wish you well.

APPENDIX I

DNA — The Template of Life

The information for all life processes is encoded in the DNA in all members of the animal and plant kingdom. Utilising the information depends on the synthesis of proteins in a highly complicated processing machine, the cell. Some primitive organisms consist of only one cell, but most animals and plants are made up of interacting systems of cells with condensed, highly specialised organs connected to the rest of the organism by vascular channels. In animals, nerves and circulating chemicals integrate the functions of the organs, the specialised functions of the brain are a predominant feature in Man. Dr Gordon Koch[31] has drawn the analogy between the DNA as the information software and the cell as the computer hardware. The information is impotent without the intricate hardware that constitutes the cell.

The DNA software is responsible for the construction and instruction of the cellular hardware and it reproduces itself. DNA is a very large stable molecule arranged in extremely long chains which are coiled on themselves in the resting nucleus of the cell, but when unravelled they are found to consist of a number of separate structures called chromosomes. In organisms that reproduce sexually the chromosomes consist of pairs that appear on microscopy to be identical, these are called homologous chromosomes, one of which will have been inherited from the father and the other from the mother. Each chromosome has a single molecule of DNA, which may be enormously long containing several million base pairs, the 'rungs' of the DNA ladder. In addition to the DNA in the chromosomes are important structural proteins which maintain the integrity of the chromosome and the expression of the genes so that they can function separately.

In the accompanying diagrams I have tried to summarise in very simplified form the structure of DNA, (*figure* 6) its manner of replication, (*figure* 8) how the cell divides under normal circumstances, mitosis (*figure* 11), and the specialised meiotic division of the sex cells in the ovary and testis (*figures* 12 & 13) that causes fresh mixing of DNA in each generation, providing variety, which is the essential requirement for evolution. In the process of meiosis in the testis, two types of sperm are produced, the X and the Y. The sperm that succeeds in fertilising the egg determines the sex of the embryo. Meiosis also involves in both sexes an exchange of genetic material between homologous chromosomes called crossing-over, so that the ova and sperms will have a mixture of paternal and maternal genes in each chromosome. There are 23 chromosomes in the ova and sperms, half the normal number, (haploid), bringing the total to 46 in Man when the ovum is fertilised (diploid).

The coding for the construction of proteins resides in the DNA and is transcribed from base triplets each consisting of three 'rungs' of the DNA ladder, one triplet for each of the

---

[31]MRC Laboratory for Molecular Biology , Cambridge

20 amino acids (*figure* 7). The proteins are the essential working tools of the cell. Each protein is composed of a specific combination of amino acids.

The whole subject of molecular biology is only forty years old starting when the structure of DNA was described by Watson and Crick. Since that time advances in our knowledge of the basic processes of the cell have been impressive and continue to accelerate extremely quickly. Portions of the DNA chain are concerned with the production of specific proteins, many of which are enzymes. These regional specialised parts of the DNA chain are called genes and they tend to move as intact entities from generation to generation. A much fuller understanding of the molecular basis of genetics will be available when the details of all the genes in human DNA have been discovered. This human genome research project is now well underway. Already surprisingly successful manipulations of human and animal DNA have become possible. This is the science of 'genetic engineering'. I hope this simplified scheme will be helpful for those unfamiliar with these vital biological concepts.

APPENDIX 2

Supplement to *Royal Society News*, November 1993

POPULATION SUMMIT OF THE WORLD'S SCIENTIFIC ACADEMIES

Representatives of national academies of science from throughout the world met in New Delhi, India from October 24-27, 1993 in a 'Science Summit' on World Population. The conference grew out of two earlier meetings, one of the Royal Society of London and the United States National Academy of Sciences, and the other an international conference organized by the Royal Swedish Academy of Sciences. Statements published by both groups[32] expressed a sense of urgent concern about the expansion of the world's population and concluded that if current predictions of population growth prove accurate and patterns of human activity on the planet remain unchanged, science and technology may not be able to prevent irreversible degradation of the environment and continued poverty for much of the world.

The New Delhi conference, organized by a group of fifteen academies[33] was convened to explore in greater detail the complex and interrelated issues of population growth, resource consumption, socio-economic development, and environmental protection. We believe it to be the first large-scale collaborative activity undertaken by the world's scientific academies.

This statement, signed by representatives of 57 academies, reflects continued concern about the intertwined problems of rapid population growth, wasteful resource consumption, environmental degradation, and poverty. In keeping with the critical focus of the conference, the statement deals primarily with population. The academies believe that ultimate success in dealing with global social, economic, and environmental problems cannot be achieved without a stable world population. The goal should be to reach zero population growth within the lifetime of our children.

---

[32] *Population Growth, Resource Consumption, and a Sustainable World*, a joint statement by the Officers of the Royal Society of London and the US National Academy of Sciences, 1992; *Statement issued by the International Conference on Population, Natural Resources and Development*, organized by the Royal Swedish Academy of Sciences and the Swedish Council for Planning and Coordination of Research, Stockholm, Sweden, 30 September - 3 October 1991; See also *An Agenda of Science for Environment and Development into the 21st Century*, based on a conference convened by the International Council of Scientific Unions in Vienna, Austria, in November 1991, Cambridge University Press, 1992; *World Scientists' Warning to Humanity*, statement signed by 1600 scientists, Union of Concerned Scientists, 1992.

[33] African Academy of Sciences, Australian Academy of Science, Brazilian Academy of Sciences, Chinese Academy of Sciences, Federation of Asian Scientific Academies and Societies, Hungarian Academy of Sciences, Indian National Science Academy, Mexican Academy of Sciences, Royal Netherlands Academy of Arts and Sciences, Pakistan Academy of Sciences, The Royal Society of London, Royal Swedish Academy of Sciences, Russian Academy of Sciences, Third World Academy of Sciences, U.S. National Academy of Sciences.

In anticipation of the approaching United Nations International Conference on Population and Development in 1994, we hope that this statement will reach the attention of governments and peoples of all countries; and contribute to further discourse and appropriate policy decisions on these complex but crucially important matters. The background for the statement is to be found in the published papers of the 1993 'Science Summit'.

1993 'SCIENCE SUMMIT' ON WORLD POPULATION: A JOINT STATEMENT BY 57[34] OF THE WORLD'S SCIENTIFIC ACADEMIES

The Growing World Population

The world is in the midst of an unprecedented expansion of human numbers. It took hundreds of thousands of years for our species to reach a population level of 10 million, only 10,000 years ago. This number grew to 100 million people about 2,000 years ago and to 2.5 billion by 1950. Within less than the span of a single lifetime, it has more than doubled to 5.5 billion in 1993.

This accelerated population growth resulted from rapidly lowered death rates (particularly infant and child mortality rates), combined with sustained high birth rates. Success in reducing death rates is attributable to several factors: increases in food production and distribution, improvements in public health (water and sanitation) and in medical technology (vaccines and antibiotics), along with gains in education and standards of living within many developing nations.

Over the last 30 years, many regions of the world have also dramatically reduced birth rates. Some have already achieved family sizes small enough, if maintained, to result eventually in a halt to population growth. These successes have led to a slowing of the world's rate of population increase. The shift from high to low death and birth rates has been called the 'demographic transition.'

The rate at which the demographic transition progresses worldwide will determine the ultimate level of the human population. The lag between downward shifts of death and birth rates may be many decades or even several generations, and during these periods population growth will continue inexorably. We face the prospect of a further doubling of the population within the next half century. Most of this growth will take place in developing countries.

Consider three hypothetical scenarios[35] for the levels of human population in the century ahead:

1. Fertility declines within sixty years from the current rate of 3.3 to a global replacement average of 2.1 children per woman. The current population momentum would lead to at least 11 billion people before levelling off at the end of the 21st century.

[34]Now 59

[35] Population Reference Bureau, *The UN Long-Range Population Projections: What they Tell Us*, Washington, D.C., 1992

2. Fertility reduces to an average of 1.7 children per woman early in the next century. Human population growth would peak at 7.8 billion persons in the middle of the 21st century and decline slowly thereafter.

3. Fertility declines to no lower than 2.5 children per woman. Global population would grow to 19 billion by the year 2100, and to 28 billion by 2150.

The actual outcome will have enormous implications for the human condition and for the natural environment on which all life depends.

Key Determinants of Population Growth

High fertility rates have historically been strongly correlated with poverty, high childhood mortality rates, low status and low educational levels of women, deficiencies in reproductive health services, and inadequate availability and acceptance of contraceptives. Falling fertility rates and the demographic transition are generally associated with improved standards of living, such as increased *per capita* incomes, increased life expectancy, lowered infant mortality, increased adult literacy, and higher rates of female education and employment.

Even with improved economic conditions, nations, regions, and societies will experience different demographic patterns due to varying cultural influences. The value placed upon large families (especially among under-privileged rural populations in less developed countries who benefit least from the process of development), the assurance of security for the elderly, the ability of women to control reproduction, and the status and rights of women within families and within societies are significant cultural factors affecting family size and the demand for family planning services.

Even with a demand for family planning services, the adequate availability of and access to family planning and other reproductive health services are essential in facilitating slowing of the population growth rate. Also, access to education and the ability of women to determine their own economic security influences their reproductive decisions.

Population Growth, Resource Consumption, and the Environment

Throughout history and especially during the twentieth century, environmental degradation has primarily been a product of our efforts to secure improved standards of food, clothing, shelter, comfort, and recreation for growing numbers of people. The magnitude of the threat to the ecosystem is linked to human population size and resource use per person. Resource use, waste production and environmental degradation are accelerated by population growth. They are further exacerbated by consumption habits, certain technological developments, and particular patterns of social organization and resource management.

As human numbers further increase, the potential for irreversible changes of far reaching magnitude also increases. Indicators of severe environmental stress include the growing loss of biodiversity, increasing greenhouse gas emissions, increasing deforestation worldwide, stratospheric ozone depletion, acid rain, loss of topsoil, and shortages of water, food, and fuel-wood in many parts of the world.

While both developed and developing countries have contributed to global environmental problems, developed countries with 85% of the gross world product and 23% of its population account for the largest part of mineral and fossil-fuel consumption, resulting in significant environmental impacts. With current technologies, present levels of consumption by the developed world are likely to lead to serious negative consequences for all countries. This is especially apparent with the increases in atmospheric carbon dioxide and trace gases that have accompanied industrialization, which have the potential for changing global climate and raising sea level.

In both rich and poor countries, local environmental problems arise from direct pollution from energy use and other industrial activities, inappropriate agricultural practices, population concentration, inadequate environmental management, and inattention to environmental goals. When current economic production has been the overriding priority and inadequate attention has been given to environmental protection, local environmental damage has led to serious negative impacts on health and major impediments to future economic growth. Restoring the environment, even where still possible, is far more expensive and time consuming than managing it wisely in the first place; even rich countries have difficulty in affording extensive environmental remediation efforts.

The relationships between human population, economic development, and the natural environment are complex. Examination of local and regional case studies reveals the influence and interaction of many variables. For example, environmental and economic impacts vary with population composition and distribution, and with rural-urban and international migrations. Furthermore, poverty and lack of economic opportunities stimulate faster population growth and increase incentives for environmental degradation by encouraging exploitation of marginal resources.

Both developed and developing countries face a great dilemma in reorienting their productive activities in the direction of a more harmonious interaction with nature. This challenge is accentuated by the uneven stages of development. If all people of the world consumed fossil fuels and other natural resources at the rate now characteristic of developed countries (and with current technologies), this would greatly intensify our already unsustainable demands on the biosphere. Yet development is a legitimate expectation of less developed and transitional countries.

The Earth is Finite

The growth of population over the last half century was for a time matched by similar world-wide increases in utilizable resources. However, in the last decade food production from both land and sea has declined relative to population growth. The area of agricultural land has shrunk, both through soil erosion and reduced possibilities of irrigation. The availability of water is already a constraint in some countries. These are warnings that the earth is finite, and that natural systems are being pushed ever closer to their limits.

Quality of Life and the Environment

Our common goal is improving the quality of life for all people, those living today and succeeding generations, ensuring their social, economic, and personal well-being with guarantees of fundamental human rights; and allowing them to live harmoniously with a protected environment. We believe that this goal can be achieved, provided we are willing to undertake the requisite social change. Given time, political will, and intelligent use of science and technology, human ingenuity can remove many constraints on improving human welfare worldwide, finding substitutes for wasteful practices, and protecting the natural environment.

But time is short and appropriate policy decisions are urgently needed. The ability of humanity to reap the benefits of its ingenuity depends on its skill in governance and management, and on strategies for dealing with problems such as widespread poverty; increased numbers of aged persons; inadequate health care and limited educational opportunities for large groups of people; limited capital for investment; environmental degradation in every region of the world; and unmet needs for family planning services in both developing and developed countries. In our judgement, humanity's ability to deal successfully with its social, economic, and environmental problems will require the achievement of zero population growth within the lifetime of our children.

Human Reproductive Health

The timing and spacing of pregnancies are important for the health of the mother, her children, and her family. Most maternal deaths are due to unsafe practices in terminating pregnancies, a lack of readily available services for high-risk pregnancies, and women having too many children or having them too early and too late in life.

Millions of people still do not have adequate access to family planning services and suitable contraceptives. Only about one-half of married couples of reproductive age are currently practising contraception. Yet as the director-general of UNICEF put it, 'Family planning could bring more benefits to more people at less cost than any other single technology now available to the human race.' Existing contraceptive methods could go far toward alleviating the unmet need if they were available and used in sufficient numbers, through a variety of channels of distribution, sensitively adapted to local needs.

But most contraceptives are for use by women, who consequently bear the risks to health. The development of contraceptives for male use continues to lag. Better contraceptives are needed for both men and women, but developing new contraceptive approaches is slow and financially unattractive to industry. Further work is needed on an ideal spectrum of contraceptive methods that are safe; efficacious; easy to use and deliver; reasonably priced; user-controlled and responsive; appropriate for special population and age cohorts; reversible; and at least some of which protect against sexually transmitted diseases, including AIDS.

Reducing fertility rates, however, cannot be achieved merely by providing more contraceptives. The demand for these services has to be addressed. Even when family planning and other reproductive health services are widely available, the social and economic status of women affects individual decisions to use them. The ability of women to make decisions about family size is greatly affected by gender roles within society and in sexual relationships. Ensuring equal opportunity for women in all aspects of society is crucial.

Thus all reproductive health services must be implemented as a part of broader strategies to raise the quality of human life. They must include the following:

- efforts to reduce and eliminate gender-based inequalities. Women and men should have equal opportunities and responsibilities in sexual, social, and economic life
- provision of convenient family planning and other reproductive health services with a wide variety of safe contraceptive options, irrespective of an individual's ability to pay
- encouragement of voluntary approaches to family planning and elimination of unsafe and coercive practices
- development policies that address basic needs such as clean water, sanitation, broad primary health care measures and education, and that foster empowerment of the poor and women.

'The adoption of a smaller family norm, with consequent decline in total fertility, should not be viewed only in demographic terms. It means that people, and particularly women, are empowered and are taking control of their fertility and the planning of their lives; it means that children are born by choice, not by chance, and that births are better planned; and it means that families are able to invest relatively more in a smaller number of beloved children, trying to prepare them for a better future.[36]

Sustainability of the Natural World As Everyone's Responsibility

In addressing environmental problems, all countries face hard choices. This is particularly so when it is perceived that there are short-term trade-offs between economic growth and environmental protection, and where there are limited financial resources. But the downside risks to the earth — our environmental life support system — over the next generation and beyond are too great to ignore. Current trends in environmental degradation from human activities combined with the unavoidable increase in global population will take us into unknown territory.

Others factors, such as inappropriate governmental policies, also contribute in nearly every case. Many environmental problems in both rich and poor countries

---

[36] Mahmond F. Fathalla, 'Family Planning and Reproductive Health: A Global Overview,' invited paper presented at the 1993 Science Summit, New Delhi, India, 26 October 1993

term economic grounds. If a longer-term view is taken, environmental goals assume an even higher priority.

The prosperity and technology of the industrialized countries give them greater opportunities and greater responsibility for addressing environmental problems worldwide. Their resources make it easier to forestall and to ameliorate local environmental problems. Developed countries need to become more efficient in both resource use and environmental protection, and to encourage an ethic that eschews wasteful consumption. If prices, taxes, and regulatory policies include environmental costs, consumption habits will be influenced. The industrialized countries need to assist developing countries and communities with funding and expertise in combating both global and local environmental problems. 'Mobilizing technology for environment' should be an integral part of this new ethic of sustainable development.

For all governments it is essential to incorporate environmental goals at the outset in legislation, economic planning, and priority setting; and to provide appropriate incentives for public and private institutions, communities, and individuals to operate in environmentally benign ways. Tradeoffs between environmental and economic goals can be reduced through wise policies. For global environmental problems, all countries of the world need to work collectively through treaties and conventions, as has occurred with such issues as global climate change and biodiversity, and to develop innovative financing mechanisms that facilitate environmental protection.

What Science and Technology Can Contribute Toward Enhancing The Human Prospect

As scientists cognizant of the history of scientific progress and aware of the potential of science for contributing to human welfare, it is our collective judgement that continuing population growth poses a great risk to humanity. Furthermore, it is not prudent to rely on science and technology alone to solve problems created by rapid population growth, wasteful resource consumption, and poverty.

The natural and social sciences are nevertheless crucial for developing new understanding so that governments and other institutions can act more effectively, and for developing new options for limiting population growth, protecting the natural environment, and improving the quality of human life. Scientists, engineers, and health professionals should study and provide advice on:

1. Cultural, social, economic, religious, educational, and political factors that affect reproductive behaviour, family size, and successful family planning

2. Conditions for human development including the impediments that result from economic inefficiencies; social inequalities; and ethnic, class, or gender biases

3. Global and local environmental change (affecting climate, biodiversity, soils, water, air), its causes (including the roles of poverty, population growth, economic growth, technology, national and international politics), and policies to mitigate its effects

4. Strategies and tools for improving all aspects of education and human resource development, with special attention to women

5. Improved family planning programs, contraceptive options for both sexes, and other reproductive health services, with special attention to needs of women, and improved general primary health care, especially maternal and child health care

6. Transitions to economies that provide increased human welfare with less consumption of energy and materials

7. Improved mechanisms for building indigenous capacity in the natural sciences, engineering, medicine, social sciences, and management in developing countries, including an increased capability of conducting integrated interdisciplinary assessments of societal issues

8. Technologies and strategies for sustainable development (agriculture, energy, resource use, pollution control, materials recycling, environmental management and protection)

9. Networks, treaties, and conventions that protect the global commons

10. Strengthened world-wide exchanges of scientists in education, training, and research.

Action is Needed Now

Humanity is approaching a crisis point with respect to the interlocking issues of population, environment, and development. Scientists today have the opportunity and responsibility to mount a concerted effort to confront our human predicament. But science and technology can only provide tools and blueprints for action and social change. It is the governments and international decision-makers, including those meeting in Cairo next September at the United Nations International Conference on Population and Development, who hold the key to our future. We urge them to take incisive action now and to adopt an integrated policy on population and sustainable development on a global scale. With each year's delay the problems become more acute. Let 1994 be remembered as the year when the people of the world decided to act together for the benefit of future generations.

The Summit Statement has been endorsed by the following organizations:

ACADEMY OF SCIENCES OF ALBANIA
AUSTRALIAN ACADEMY OF SCIENCE
AUSTRIAN ACADEMY OF SCIENCES
BANGLADESH ACADEMY OF SCIENCES
ACADEMY OF SCIENCES OF BALARUS
NATIONAL ACADEMY OF SCIENCES OF BOLIVIA
BRAZILIAN ACADEMY OF SCIENCES
BULGARIAN ACADEMY OF SCIENCES
ROYAL SOCIETY OF CANADA
CARIBBEAN ACADEMY OF SCIENCES
CHINESE ACADEMY OF SCIENCES
COLUMBIAN ACADEMY OF EXACT, PHYSICAL, AND NATURAL SCIENCES
CROATIAN ACADEMY OF SCIENCES AND ARTS
CUBAN ACADEMY OF SCIENCES
ACADEMY OF SCIENCES OF THE CZECH REPUBLIC
ROYAL DANISH ACADEMY OF SCIENCES AND LETTERS
ACADEMY OF SCIENTIFIC RESEARCH AND TECHNOLOGY, EGYPT
ESTONIAN ACADEMY OF SCIENCES
FEDERATION OF ASIAN SCIENTIFIC ACADEMIES AND SOCIETIES
DELEGATION OF THE FINNISH ACADEMIES OF SCIENCE AND LETTERS
FRENCH ACADEMY OF SCIENCES
CONFERENCE OF THE GERMAN ACADEMIES OF SCIENCES
GHANA ACADEMY OF ARTS AND SCIENCES
ACADEMY OF ATHENS, GREECE
HUNGARIAN ACADEMY OF SCIENCES
INDIAN NATIONAL SCIENCE ACADEMY
IRANIAN ACADEMY OF SCIENCES
ISRAEL ACADEMY OF SCIENCES AND HUMANITIES

KAZAKHSTAN NATIONAL ACADEMY OF SCIENCES
ROYAL SCIENTIFIC SOCIETY, JORDAN
KENYA NATIONAL ACADEMY OF SCIENCES
NATIONAL ACADEMY OF SCIENCES, REPUBLIC OF KOREA
LATVIAN ACADEMY OF SCIENCES
LITHUANIAN ACADEMY OF SCIENCES
MACEDONIAN ACADEMY OF SCIENCES AND ARTS
MALAYSIAN SCIENTIFIC ASSOCIATION
NATIONAL ACADEMY OF SCIENCES, MEXICO
ACADEMY OF SCIENCES OF MOLDOVA
MONGOLIAN ACADEMY OF SCIENCES
ACADEMY OF THE KINGDOM OF MOROCCO
ROYAL NEPAL ACADEMY OF SCIENCE AND TECHNOLOGY
ROYAL NETHERLANDS ACADEMY OF ARTS AND SCIENCES
NIGERIAN ACADEMY OF SCIENCE
NORWEGIAN ACADEMY OF SCIENCE AND LETTERS
PAKISTAN ACADEMY OF SCIENCES
NATIONAL ACADEMY OF SCIENCE AND TECHNOLOGY, PHILIPPINES
POLISH ACADEMY OF SCIENCES
ROMANIAN ACADEMY OF SCIENCES
RUSSIAN ACADEMY OF SCIENCES
SLOVAK ACADEMY OF SCIENCES
SLOVENIAN ACADEMY OF SCIENCES AND ARTS
ROYAL SWEDISH ACADEMY OF SCIENCES
CONFERENCE OF THE SWISS SCIENTIFIC ACADEMIES
THIRD WORLD ACADEMY OF SCIENCES
UGANDA NATIONAL ACADEMY OF SCIENCE AND TECHNOLOGY
UKRAINIAN ACADEMY OF SCIENCES
ROYAL SOCIETY OF LONDON
NATIONAL ACADEMY OF SCIENCES OF THE UNITED STATES OF AMERICA
NATIONAL ACADEMY OF PHYSICS, MATHEMATICS, AND NATURAL SCIENCES OF
    VENEZUELA

Suggestions for Further Reading

ALLEN, Mea: *Darwin and his Flowers,* Faber & Faber, 1977

CAREY, John: *The Intellectual and the Masses*, Faber & Faber, 1992

DARWIN, Charles: *The Voyage of the Beagle*, Everyman, 1906

DAVIDSON, James Dale & MOGG, William Rees: *The Great Reckoning*, Sidgewick & Jackson, 1991

DAWKINS, Richard: *The Selfish Gene*, Oxford University Press, 1976

DAWKINS, Richard: *The Blind Watchmaker,* Penguin 1988

DIAMOND, Jared: *The Rise and Fall of the Third Chimpanzee*, Vintage, 1992

DJERASSI, Carl: *The Pill, Pygmy Chimps, and Degas' Horse*, Basic Books, 1992

EHRLICH, Paul and Anne: *The Population Explosion*, Hutchinson, 1990

ENZENSBERGER, Hans Magnus: The Great Migration, Winter, 1992

GLEICK, James: *Genius. Richard Feynman and Modern Physics*, Little, Brown & Company, 1992

KENNEDY, Paul: *Preparing for the 21st Century*, Harper Collins, 1993

KRUUK, Hans: *The Spotted Hyena. A study of preditation and social behaviour*, University of Chicago Press, 1972

LEVI, Tom: *A Very Human Adventure*, Synchron Associates, 1992

MOOREHEAD, Alan: *Darwin and the Beagle*, Penguin, 1971

OLBY, Robert C: *The Origins of Mendelism*, Constable & Company Ltd, 1966

PIEL, Gerard: *Only One World*, W.H. Freeman, NY 1992

SELBOURNE, David: *The Spirit of the Age*, Sinclair Stevenson, 1993

WALTHER, Ingo E: *Paul Gauguin*, Benedikt Taschen Verlag, 1992

WATSON, James D: *The Double Helix*, Penguin, 1970

WILLIAMS-ELLIS, Amabel: *Darwin's Moon*, Blackie, 1966

WINCH,Donald: *Malthus*, Oxford University Press, 1987

WOLPERT, Lewis: *The Unnatural Nature of Science*, Faber & Faber, 1992

FABIAN, A.C:*ORIGINS - Darwin College Lectures*, Cambridge University Press, 1988

'Reproductive Health: a key to a brighter future,' World Health Organisation Biennial Report, 1990-91

Suggestions for Further Reading